Tish

Tish

CISSIE MILLER

DOUBLEDAY & COMPANY, INC.

GARDEN CITY, NEW YORK

1981

All of the characters in this book
are fictitious, and any resemblance
to actual persons, living or dead,
is purely coincidental.

Library of Congress Cataloging in Publication Data

Coy, Stanlee Miller.
Tish.

I. Title.
PS3553.O949T5   813'.54
AACR2
ISBN: 0-385-17468-3
Library of Congress Catalog Card Number 81–43049

First Edition

To Charles and Imelda,
the sun and moon to me.

Tish

CHAPTER 1

"By all that's holy, what trick is this?" The rider cursed as he applied all of his skill to subduing his wildly plunging horse. He yanked in the reins until the bit strained against the black steed's sensitive mouth, and at the same time he flicked his whip against the horse's flanks as reproof for his frantic rearing. Instantly, because force was rare between master and horse, the animal quieted. The rider leaned forward and patted the trembling but quiescent horse.

"A fog as thick as hell's smoke I expected to find in this godforsaken place," he murmured soothingly into the still-twitching ears, "but I would not have thought to receive a bath of . . . of?"

Through the paper-thin leather of his glove he fingered the object that had literally fallen from the sky. But it was impossible! A piece of fabric had plummeted down, half covering and thus blinding and terrifying the horse. Instinctively the man had grabbed it away and instinctively had kept hold of it even while concentrating on calming the animal. How in God's name could a piece of fabric assault one from the sky? It was so inexplicable, so unexpected, that the horse, trained by his master to ignore cannon fire and far worse on countless battlefields, had nearly shaken loose the rider and bolted.

"No use continuing on, Tarquin, in any case. This mountain trail that calls itself a road is more suited to a donkey or a goat than to a horse. We have perforce gone so slowly and have taken so many turns and twists in this fog that we are quite lost." The big stallion tossed his head as though in agreement and blew forcefully through his nostrils.

The rider leaped easily to the ground. The fog had thickened quickly in the last few moments and it was as though all the candles in a room were suddenly snuffed. He could scarcely see an arm's length in front and gropingly, cautiously, man and horse inched forward until the narrow, stony path widened a few feet with a minuscule grassy border against the rocks of the hill. It was unnecessary to tether the animal, for he responded to his master's voice better than to a bridle.

"What we can't change we must endure, old friend," the man said softly, extracting a handful of sugar cubes from his saddlebag and gently stroking the steed's long nose as he fed him. "The wisest strategy now is to wait. We have shared worse accommodations."

He shook his head quizzically as he studied the object that had assaulted them. The light in the moist, dense fog was a dim gray and the fabric also was dark so that it might for all the world have been an optical illusion. Except that it was real. And it was? A woman's gown!

Wrapping his cloak more firmly around his shoulders, the man stretched out against the rocky incline. No greater puzzle had ever come his way and he was nothing short of astounded. But he had learned the hard way that a prudent soldier does not waste energy in fruitless endeavors or speculations. And so he tossed the frock to one side, pulled his hat lower over his ears, put the puzzle firmly from his mind, and slept.

The habits of combat were still fresh and in the very moment of being awakened by the strange sound the man sprang up, instantly alert, instantly wary. It was not a sound he could identify. Thumping noises, irregular, growing louder, as though a heavy sack were being dragged in bouncing jerks along the trail by a giant? The man smiled slightly, his eyes intensely studying the opaque gray shade that still rendered the countryside invisible. The horse whinnied nervously.

"It's all right, Tarquin," he whispered. "There is nothing mortal man can invent that we fear, and this is certainly more interesting than most country travels. But what the devil is it?"

"Ow! Ow! Won't that infernal anchor take hold?" The scraping, shuddering noises and the voice were coming closer.

"Are you in trouble?" the man called out.

"Owwwwww!" was the response to a louder thump and a sort of dragging, rasping sound.

"Are you in trouble?" he repeated.

"I am being shaken to bits, you hen-brained person! Do something! Here!"

Like a blind man, one foot testing the solidity of the ground before he stepped, the man advanced toward the voice. He had earned a chestful of medals for bravery, but that did not mean he was foolhardy enough to stride into the grayness ahead when it might conceal a precipice.

"If you would be so kind as to give me a hand, I should be grateful." The formal phrase dripped sarcasm but the effect was diminished by the involuntary hiccups of the speaker. "Hurry."

If twelve regiments of Napoleon's finest had suddenly appeared, the man could not have been more surprised. In front of him he perceived a lurching, bouncing wicker basket, heaving and rocking by some unknown power, and in the basket, a half-dressed female!

"Thank heaven," she gasped. "You took long enough. Here, grab this." She tossed him a rope. "Tie it as tightly as you can to that tree there. No! That one!" she commanded. "Then help me climb out before my teeth are shaken from my head and whatever bones are not broken already shatter to pieces."

He did as directed, without comment. It was no small task

securing the rope, for whatever force moved the basket pulled and tugged mightily against the constraint. But finally it was done. Then he turned to the female who scrambled unceremoniously over the rim of the basket and fell into his arms. Involuntarily, he tightened his grip, but he was not looking down at the rescued victim. His eyes gazed skyward, following ropes leading upward from the basket.

"By God, it's a balloon!"

"In that at least you show some sense," the female said bitingly. "Now put me down."

Thick black eyebrows drew together and brown-green eyes darkened thunderously at her imperious behavior, though that sign of temper was contradicted by a faint quirk of his wide mouth.

"You are mighty free with orders, madam, and short with thanks." His hold on her tightened a fraction.

He was clearly laughing at her and the female reddened, not with a girlish blush of confusion but with rage. "I thank you for helping me, sir," she hissed. She drew a deep breath. "Please, put me down."

He studied her face. She was not a beauty. Fairness was all the rage in London and this was no pink-and-gold charmer. Her brown, waist-length hair hung straight and her eyes were brown also, though the lashes were long enough and curly enough to satisfy society's strictest requirements. She was like a colt, he thought, quivering in his arms not from nervousness or shyness but from a sort of inner spring of tension, a creature poised to take flight. And like a colt she was slender, with delicate bones and long limbs. He himself was well over six foot and she was an armful. Not conventionally beautiful, but striking. Memorable.

"You are short also on clothes," he added, his eyes roving deliberately over her white linen chemise and petticoat. A few small pink bows added adornment but there was no lace. The linen was of fine quality, he noted, and he was an acknowledged expert at ladies' finery of all sorts. He should be, having paid for enough of it to outfit a dozen high steppers. His present fair Cyprian was the toast of London's stage and she boasted that, like a queen, she never wore the same garments twice. A low laugh startled him from his wandering thoughts.

"I was recalling your face when you first saw me," the girl admitted. "I daresay I am a bit unconventionally clad. More the reason, then, to put me down. Please. And besides," she added ruefully, "I have been tossed about like a beanbag for so long that if I do not put my feet on terra firma at once, I cannot answer for the behavior of my stomach."

She chuckled again as her threat had instant effect. He almost threw her down. And the mask of equanimity that he habitually wore slipped a fraction at her frankness. Well-bred females didn't even admit to possessing stomachs, much less confess to potential digestive disasters!

"That's better. You need have no fear that I shall disgrace myself further. And you cannot imagine what a welcome thing it is to feel those rough pebbles digging into my slippers." She glanced up anxiously. Thin fingers of sunlight were tearing into the fog and the full height of the balloon was becoming visible.

Four or five feet above the yellow wicker basket, secured by a dozen thick ropes, a gaily striped orb of yellow and blue rose some fifty feet into the air. The wind had diminished with the fog and the balloon swayed lazily now against the slight breeze.

"I don't believe it's damaged," the girl mused aloud. "We can be thankful for that."

"And what of you?" The mask was once more firmly in place and he looked and sounded as though he were addressing an acquaintance met strolling in Vauxhall Gardens. "Are *you* damaged?"

"I have some scrapes." She demonstrated a long streak of red along one arm and numerous scratches on both of her hands. "And I expect I shall be sore as anything tomorrow with a dozen bruises on each inch, but no, nothing seems to have broken." She waggled each foot experimentally.

"There was one especially fierce thump the first time I hit ground and I thought I felt something crack here," she ran her hands matter-of-factly down her ribs, "but it must have been the basket, not me. Thank the Lord it wasn't demolished."

She shivered slightly, turning an expectant face toward the ever-brighter sun. "It will be clear as crystal in a few minutes," she promised. "The weather changes quickly here in the Lake District."

Her shiver triggered a suppressed oath. He had actually forgotten she was undressed.

"May I offer you my cloak?"

"Yes, please." Her eyes twinkled. "If only for propriety if not the chill." She flung the cloak about her shoulders and went off toward the balloon without a backward glance. She was examining the basket from all sides when the man reappeared and offered her the gown that had nearly cost him a bad accident.

"That *is* lucky," she said casually, keeping her attention on the basket. "It's not new but I haven't another half so comfortable."

"I'm glad to see you aren't burdened with false modesty." For some unknown reason her nonchalance in this most unconventional situation infuriated him.

She bit back a retort and deliberately handed him the cloak before slipping into the gown. Then she reached deep into the basket, extracted an old black spencer, and made a show of buttoning it firmly to the chin before replying.

"I do not make a practice of roaming the countryside without clothes. Expediency forced me to cast off my gown.

"However, I dare say you have seen much more of the female form from highly proper society ladies in London who wear muslins and silks that are virtually transparent. And who go so far as to dampen their gowns so as to make them cling. The excuse is that their gowns are in the classic style and that when dampened they cling as tightly as the folds on a Grecian statue. Ha!" she laughed derisively. "My undergarments are certainly not my customary attire, but they are neither transparent nor the least bit clinging. In fact, they are much more modest than what fashion dictates is the proper attire for a ball!"

She took a deep breath and concluded, her voice louder and higher. "If I have shocked you, and from your manner I gather you are unused to mixing much in society, then I sincerely beg your pardon. And you need not waste your time further by lingering here. Things are quite under control now. Good day, sir."

She could not be more than twenty but she had delivered the scathing scolding as though she were a dowager of ninety and he a green boy. He bristled at her haughty dismissal but answered lightly. He intended to have the last word.

"You are right on all counts and I deserved that set-down. I beg your pardon." He swept a lazy bow. "But you must grant that yours is an uncommon apparition—even in a fog.

"I admit I lost my sense of perspective," he continued with a self-deprecating smile, "but you must not lay all the blame at my door. You were such a delicious armful to be rescued, my wits were understandably addled."

The self-deprecating smile, the charming apology, the flattery, were all obviously lost on the young lady because she dismissed them with a shrug and asked fretfully, "Whatever do you suppose has become of Bowen?"

Thick black brows drew together again and this time his entire expression was thunderous. He had been spared female rebuffs since coming of age, protected against failure by the fact of possessing a huge fortune, an impressive title, and an equally impressive appearance. Not that he was picture-book handsome. His aquiline nose was slightly bent from an early, untutored foray into fisticuffs, his brows were too thick and fierce to suit his face, and his shoulders broader than they should be in proper proportion to his height, tall as he was. But such were his charm and forcefulness that he could, when he desired, dazzle any female into thinking he was Adonis. That plus money and title had served to carry all his conquests to a successful conclusion. Save this one. And she not only rebuffed him, she ignored him!

"Who is Bowen? And what is this contraption doing here? I think I am entitled to an explanation."

She gave him a startled look but her firm chin rose into the air.

"Allow me to begin with introductions," he continued. "I am the Earl of Ardenly."

Her chin ascended another millimeter but the girl could not resist the definite command in those curious brown-green eyes.

"I am Letitia Abbott, *Lady* Letitia Abbott. Bowen is the man who helps me. And that—that contraption is, as you observed earlier, a balloon." She faltered as his mouth tightened, his expression grew even more thunderous, and he took a menacing step toward her.

"And—" he prompted.

"And I was riding in it. As you saw. It is a captive balloon. Or, rather, it was. It was attached by a very thick rope so that it can only rise to a height of a thousand feet. Grand-père thought it best to have a trial in a tethered balloon before we venture on a free flight." She waved vaguely toward the east.

"Grand-père? And just where is Grand-père now?"

"Well, he's probably frantic with worry."

"Where?" he snapped.

"At home," she replied with exasperation. "He couldn't come with me. He has wrenching arthritis, poor dear. It's a common ailment among aeronauts, you know. The dampness of the clouds, for one thing. And being subject to sudden rainstorms."

"And not being fit to go himself," the man interjected, "your dear Grand-père allowed you to racket about the skies in that—that contraption and risk death or disfigurement as you bounce toward earth!"

"So far as bouncing toward earth goes," she said with considerable hauteur, "experienced aeronauts consider every balloon descent to be a matter of concern. There are so many elements subject to chance. But you cannot blame Grand-père for the rope's snapping. He could not have anticipated that!"

"Where balloons are concerned, one should always anticipate disaster," he warned. "But tell me just what happened."

She sighed and thrust her hands behind her back, but not before he noticed that they were trembling.

"At first I couldn't believe the rope had snapped. I was astounded. And for a moment or two I simply drifted. I literally couldn't move. Then I realized the balloon was rising quite fast and I knew I had to do something. So I opened the valve to release gas—so that it would go down, of course. But in my excitement I released too much gas too quickly. I went down awfully fast. It seemed only seconds before I was nearing the ground and I feared I was going to crash in a thicket of trees." She winced but went on.

"Actually, I was pleased to note that I grew very calm at that point. I understood that I had to halt the descent immediately. So I heaved out the bags of sand, which helped at once. Only, the balloon continued to fall rather fast. And I tossed out the basket of food. Nanny had packed an enormous picnic of cheese and apples and bread. And naturally a bottle of brandy. Then I tossed out the cushions. And the telescope and maps. The basket was pulled up enough then to just skim the treetops. Only, a sudden downdraft hit. There was nothing else left to throw out. That's when I took off my gown and let that go. I scooted over the last tree, and even though the fog was growing thicker I could see that the treetops were preferable to what lay ahead." Her voice lowered dramatically.

"I was heading smack for the mountainside! That's when I threw out the anchor and though it caught and kept us from the rocks, the balloon and I did bounce at the end of the rope like a trout on a line. And here I am," she concluded stoutly. "Nothing to be concerned about."

"You are a born storyteller," he commented dourly.

"Thank you. I do think I have a gift for narrative. Though that little adventure isn't a matter of great concern, as I said."

"Of course it's a matter of concern! I have seen various balloon demonstrations in Vauxhall Gardens and the Crystal Palace in London. Like every passing fad, balloon ascensions have attracted a vast amount of attention from the public. Indeed, I even took a trip myself, merely to confirm my assumptions."

"You've taken a ride?" she interrupted. "In a free balloon?"

"Yes," he snapped. "And as I had anticipated, a balloon is a capricious, senseless object and therefore it is no wonder that a descent in one is a matter of concern. When I travel I like to know where I am going, to direct my steps, not to be borne aloft like a feather, subject to the slightest breeze, the faintest caprice of nature. But that is not the issue.

"The issue is that you might have been killed today. Or brutally hurt. And your grandfather has apparently lost any trace of common sense in allowing you to hazard such danger. No female should be buffeted about as you were."

"Grand-père is a fine and noble gentleman," she said frostily. "In any case, my well-being is none of your concern."

"You made it my concern when you called for help!"

A shout from the hillside below distracted them both and cut short the altercation.

"It's Bowen," Letitia said thankfully. "Everything is all right now."

"What happens now?" the man inquired coldly.

"He's brought a wagon, you see," she answered with equal chill. "We load the basket aboard and that's the end of it for today."

"And the balloon follows you home like a stray puppy?"

"If it has not lost too much gas, then we can lead it home. By the anchor rope. Otherwise we deflate it altogether and pack it aboard the wagon. I hope we shall not have to do that, for it is a great trouble filling it up again. Bowen is very strong," she added pointedly. "He will do what must be done."

The person thus described, toiling up the steep, mountain road, was not tall but he was big-boned, a farmer by the looks of him, and obviously equal to gathering in the errant balloon and its basket.

"We shall not detain you further, my lord."

The man hesitated. "I became slightly confused in the fog," he ventured reluctantly. "Kendal is toward the east, of course. And is this the road to Grasmere?"

The girl was clearly surprised by something, but she flashed an impish grin. "You do not know where to direct your steps? How galling for a man who likes to know where he is at all times." She flushed then at the quelling stare her flippant remark evoked. "This is the road. Grasmere is just over the other side of the mountain."

He nodded curtly. "Good day, then, Lady Letitia."

"Good day, my lord."

He retreated to find Tarquin, mounted and rode off without a backward glance. Before the horse had time to break into a trot they had achieved the hilltop, and the man reined in the animal sharply. Travel accounts were not his sort of reading and he had largely ignored the recent enthusiasm and vogue for the Lake District. The northern reaches of England were altogether too damp and variable in climate for the taste of a man born and bred in the gentle, soothing clime of Somerset. But the scene below was undeniably lovely. The vale was almost entirely ringed by high pastures and hills. The vale itself was not large but it was flat, green and lush with a good-sized lake in the middle, the water so crystalline that in reflecting the now bright, cloudless sky above, it might have been blue glass. The small village of Grasmere spilled out upon one hill, a cluster of whitewashed stone houses framed in green. In the distance, at the far north end of the valley, stood the one imposing structure to be seen, and it was toward that estate that the man now spurred his horse. Anxious to terminate his unsettling trip, he pressured the steed with his knees and urged him, without resort to spurs or whip, into a fast gallop. The speed was cathartic and the road, now widening as it descended, reverberated with the sound of thundering hooves.

CHAPTER 2

The Marquess of Lansdale, George Glines, paced the length of the great gold-and-rose drawing room as he listened to his friend's account of his travels.

"It must be Tish," he exploded. "I tell you, Ali, no other female in these parts fits your description and no other female in the whole of England would fall in with such a mad scheme. It must be Tish!"

Alexander Grenfell, the Earl of Ardenly, reached for a crystal decanter that had been placed conveniently at his elbow. "There's no need to become agitated," he said calmly. "I think a glass of your excellent cognac is in order for us both. Come, sit, and tell me about this incomparable Tish."

Lord Lansdale flung himself down on one of a pair of deep chairs flanking the fireplace. "I do feel a bit unsettled," he admitted. He drained the brandy at one gulp and reached out to have his glass refilled. "Didn't she tell you her name?"

"I had forgotten, but yes, she did. And it was Lady Letitia Abbott. Obviously your Tish."

Lansdale nodded gloomily.

"This is an amusing mystery, George. Nothing to look so solemn about. Now tell me, who is this gal?"

"You'd know her father's family; they're the Abbotts from Lancaster. One of the cousins was a year or two ahead of us at Cambridge. Not a very clever chap. Didn't care much for him.

"In any case, the family curse, it seems, is a taste for gambling. One way or another most of the property has been gambled away. Tish's father, Earl of Dinsmore, is the only

male in the line who escaped from the so-called 'fatal flaw.'"
He sniffed derisively. "Point is, he is the only member of the
immediate family left who is the least bit plump in the
pocket. And he ain't got much left, but enough to carry off
the life of a diplomat. Though what he does is beyond me,
since he has been abroad on one mission or another for the
last ten years. Secret assignments, messages to foreign govern-
ments, all very hush-hush from what Tish hints. Tish's
mother is bedridden. No one ever sees her. And then there is
the grandfather."

"Yes, she mentioned her Grand-père. I am especially interested in hearing about him, old chap."

"Hmmmn. Well, he's a curious sort. For one thing, he is a
French count. His name is Henri de Saint-Pierre and he came
over from France fourteen years ago when Tish's mother had
a fit of some sort and took to her bed. You remember when
the Peace of Amiens marked a brief truce between France
and us? He came then. I suppose one of the reasons the family stays up here is that the Lake District is isolated and the
old man isn't subject here to the anti-French sentiments that
can flare so strongly in London."

"You couldn't expect the British to be enamored of the
French when Boney persisted in shooting at us," Alec said
with a small grin. "However, it still is not clear to me. If
Henri de Saint-Pierre is a count and has an English granddaughter, one would assume he would have fled France at the
time of the revolution and would have been in England since
then. As you know, those émigrés are quite popular in London society."

"Your devotion to logic has always been a consistently admirable trait," George replied, "but it doesn't apply in this
case. I told you, he only came from France fourteen years
ago, in 1802.

"Don't glower, I'll explain. Actually, it is simple enough.
The Saint-Pierres had, in fact, supported the revolution,
whether from idealism or expediency I cannot say. Then, in

ninety-two, Tish's grandmother and mother fled to England because they were disillusioned with the whole business after the September Paris massacres, when many English who had been sympathetic to the revolution also became disenchanted. Tish's mother and father met, married, and produced Tish. I don't know why the grandfather didn't come then. Perhaps he was caught. The old man doesn't have anything to do with any of us and Tish will not discuss him in detail."

"An earl is not a bad catch for a penniless émigré, even a titled one," Alec said sardonically.

After a moment's reflection, George agreed that it wasn't a bad match for the young French girl. "After all," he mused, "the Abbotts may have their unfortunate predilection toward gambling, but they are very well connected. For her side, Tish's mother is said to have been a strikingly handsome woman with a delightful charm and unforgettable personality."

"I believe that, if her offspring is any proof, but go on. The grandfather followed, you said."

"That's right. And the old man makes no bones about where his loyalties lie. Tish has admitted that much. Not that he was so devoted to Bonaparte, but he feels the English are inferior mentally. He is keen on science, it seems, and admittedly there the French have it all over us. The result is that he keeps apart, to himself. I don't think he has even learned a word of English."

Alec frowned. "And the girl? Where do her loyalties lie?"

"With England," George said flatly. "She's English through and through. Though she is also very loyal to her grandfather."

"I would think that would lead to a conflict in her feelings."

"It doesn't when she is here at Grasmere. At least that's what she insists. It was only when she was in London that she felt uncomfortable about her grandfather. She went down for a season a couple of years ago. She told me she was thrust upon one of the penniless cousins who supposedly had the social connections to introduce her to society. It was strictly a business arrangement, from the sound of it. Tish's papa would pick up the bills for a season for Tish and the cousin's daughter. Poor Tish lasted little more than a month before she packed her valise and fled home. She said life was intolerable without her mountains and lakes and sky. But I suspect it was hearing the anti-French jokes and talk that ruined it for her."

"And this ballooning? How did that start?"

"I ain't got the foggiest. Never heard of it."

The men were silent while a liveried footman moved soundlessly through the room, adding logs to the brightly blazing fire, replacing the half-empty decanter and proffering cigars from a silver box.

It was stifling in the room, Alec realized. He rose to his feet and stood back from the dancing flames.

"How old is she?"

"She's twenty-three. Her birthday is just past, May thirty-first."

"So when her mother fell ill in aught two, she was nine."

"Presumably," George said impatiently. "But what difference does that make?"

"She has been under the old gentleman's influence for most of her life."

"I told you, she is thoroughly British!" George retorted, his fingers commencing a fast, irregular tattoo on the arm of his chair. "And so far as influence goes, my own mama is something of an invalid and I promise you that she is an iron presence in this house!"

"Apparently you and Tish are in one another's confidence," Alec shrugged.

"We have little society here," the other man said defensively. "You will recall that I came home on several vacations while we were at Cambridge. Of course, Tish is several years younger than I, but Grasmere is barely a village and one has little choice of acquaintances. And even though she was only a child when she and her family first came here, she was always good company." His pleasant face lightened and he relaxed visibly, his hands quiet. "She is a crackerjack fisherman and a tireless walker. That's the main sport hereabouts, old man. Walking." He gave a whoop of laughter at his friend's exaggerated grimace of revulsion.

"I like Tish," George continued softly. "I don't always have to say flowery things, gabble about fashion or listen to gossip with Tish."

"A paragon of feminity," Alec said lightly. Then he yawned, stretching his long arms with gusto. "It's early hours, but will you forgive me if I turn in, George? It must be the country air, for I am deucedly sleepy."

"All right. Shall we take a turn outside first?"

Alec Grenfell smiled his agreement and the two men walked to double glass doors that gave onto a wide marble terrace overlooking the vale. The two friends were as opposite in appearance as night and day but they walked in evident harmony, Alec fitting his longer legs to the man's shorter stride.

Lord Lansdale's mother, who was abed with a cold and had not come down for dinner, was native to the Lake District. She had been a spectacular beauty in her youth, but her father was only a country clergyman, of respectable lineage though nothing impressive. Therefore London society had been agape when she had married the prize bachelor of the year, the wealthy Lord Lansdale. The tale of their romance was already legend in the Lake District. She was barely sixteen when they met by chance. He was touring the District with friends and had set off for a solitary walk. She had been walking alone also, on an errand for her mother, and had turned her ankle; unable to continue, she chose to sit at the edge of the road, waiting placidly for some passerby to lend her aid. Instead of a farmer's cart or boy driving a cow, the first person to pass by was a young man so handsome that he might have been a prince. And indeed, it was the Marquess. It was love at first sight, according to the story. The truth is that they were caught in one of the District's famous sudden showers and they took refuge in a grove of oak trees where they sheltered for five hours. By the time the skies cleared they were truly in love, and they married within the month despite the objections of his family. He took her to his home in Dorset but within a year she was returned with her infant son, her husband dead from a fall while hunting. Here, on an isolated hillside, she had constructed a replica of the fabulous Lansdale ancestral home. And here she still lived, her marble palace in strange juxtaposition to the humble cottages of Grasmere.

From his mother George inherited the Norse looks typical of the District. He was thin, not very tall, with a long, straight nose and blue eyes. He had the Norse character, too. Men of Norse blood had farmed the difficult Lake country for a thousand years and they were by nature aloof, though not unfriendly. And once friends, they showed their affection in deeds rather than words.

Alec was the one close friend George had made in his Cambridge days, but the two had a deeper bond than the shared remembrances of college life. Different motives had inspired them to the same determination to be part of English resistance against Bonaparte's ambitions. They had fought together in the Peninsular War and later met once more over the steaming ashes of Waterloo.

Now, only two weeks short of the first anniversary of that decisive combat, they were far removed from the smells and sights of battle. They had reentered English society to find it was virtually unchanged by the conflict that had ravaged a large part of the Continent. Of course, fashionable society had marked the war, buzzed about the battles, aped the military fashions, but it had not suffered.

"I trust you will not find it too dull here," George said impulsively, regarding his friend with some concern. "We shall find entertainment, I promise."

Alec shook his head. "My friend, there is nothing I welcome more than a spell of quiet. You remember that it was I who suggested—nay, insisted, that we both leave London and come here.

"After the war ended I imagined there was nothing I so desired as to be back home, resuming the old rounds, cards at Brooks's, friends at Almack's. And in faith no one was more enthusiastic than I about seeking out company. But, as I said before we left London, it was foolhardy to think we could pick up where we had left off as though nothing had occurred in between except a holiday tour of spas."

"But you were always wary," George reminded him. "It was I who was the fool! When I entered Paris after Waterloo it seemed a dreamland, with rivers of champagne free to any officer and endless celebratory balls with gorgeous creatures just waiting to be claimed."

"Dreams do not last," Alec smiled. "Still, you cannot pretend you did not enjoy that circus while it lasted."

"I could not forget the stench of gangrene that sickened all of Brussels," George shuddered. "Nor the puddles of blood between the crushed rows of corn."

"Neither of us shall ever forget, but we must put those memories away for a while until we can see the whole picture." Alec draped an arm about George's shoulder. "Boney was stopped. It was worthwhile!"

"Was it?" George asked listlessly.

"You know it was." Alec gave him a sharp rap on the back. "And neither of us was so sunk in melancholy that we neglected to visit our tailors upon returning to London. And, as I recall, you found yourself a sweet lass for consolation."

George smiled gratefully at Alec's rallying. "A sweet lass, I admit, but you set your marker on the best-looking new chit at the Drury Lane Theatre. And the wagers around town were that you consumed more Regent's punch than the Prince himself."

"Ughhh! Don't remind me," Alec groaned. "I vowed never to drink that damnable concoction—after supper, at least. The green tea keeps one awake. And as for that fair Cyprian, she is a beauty, true, but also an expensive frippery. Do you know what her last request was? A diamond tiara. Ha! She took her stage roles too seriously, and I vow she is not repining in solitude for me this night. Now that is putting too fine a point on our relationship!"

"I never thought you to be so shockingly tight-fisted," George teased. "You might buy that pretty bird one hundred tiaras and never feel the pinch, your purse is so full."

Chuckling, Alec leaned lower to confide something into George's ear that set him into a paroxysm of laughter. Still laughing, the two entered the house.

CHAPTER 3

"Ruddick, my dear fellow, if I hear any more complaints from you I shall pack you back to London on the next available donkey!" Alexander Grenfell studied his appearance in the pier glass as his valet handed him a snowy white linen neckcloth. Deftly, Grenfell wove the linen into an elegant arrangement. Falling just short of perfection to that critical eye, it was whipped off and tossed to the floor where it joined a heap of similar failures.

Ruddick, a mild man of small stature and obsequious manners was, in fact, so determined and so devoted to his master that he had followed him into the army, serving as his batman with courage and zest. He was at his best, however, as a valet. He could achieve a shine on his lordship's boots that was the envy of every buck on Regency Row, he could spot a wrinkle in his lordship's superfine jacket at one hundred paces and he had the tact and discretion of a prime minister. He was, nonetheless, a city creature and he felt distinctly out of sorts in the country.

"I beg Your Lordship's pardon," he said insincerely. "I am only attempting to acquaint Your Lordship with some facts which may be of service to Your Lordship."

Having finally achieved a knot that met his meticulous standards, the Earl turned to slip into his jacket. It fit, both men noted with equal satisfaction, to perfection. He was not a dandy, but snug fit was the essence of proper tailoring. If the dark-blue jacket was without a wrinkle, the yellow breeches were like a second skin. The tight-fitting breeches in turn fitted into riding boots.

"Don't 'Your Lordship' me to death, Ruddick. Just come out with it."

"I am aware that Your Lordship does not approve of gossip," the valet sighed, brushing invisible specks from those broad shoulders. "But I feel it advisable to repeat what was hinted at dinner last night in the servants' hall."

"And?"

"It was suggested that her ladyship, Lord Lansdale's mother, suffers from more than a usual number of colds."

"She is apparently a semi-invalid. What the devil does that signify?"

The valet coughed into a handkerchief. "It is unclear. Merely the hint that she is not always indisposed by colds, m'lord." He paused.

"Pursue it, Ruddick." The Earl's eyes were fixed on the mirror but unseeing. "Indeed, I abominate backstairs chatter, but I. am interested . . . for my friend's sake. Now, since you laid out these garments I presume they are appropriate for a morning walk."

"Yes m'lord." Ruddick beamed with satisfaction at the Earl's appearance in general and at his high black boots in particular. They gleamed like polished ebony.

"I should not like to appear in this rustic setting in a rig more fit for Hyde Park," his lordship said with a twinkle.

"I trust you have not had cause to complain in the past," the valet replied in an aggrieved tone.

"Your record is spotless. Thus far." And his lordship shut the door quickly behind him before his bristling manservant could frame a suitable reply.

As Lansdale Hall was an exact duplicate of the late Lord Lansdale's ancestral home in Dorset, so, too, the gardens surrounding the Hall replicated the originals. There were formal gardens, terraced with mathematical rectitude on the sloping hillside; prim, patterned flower beds, straight paths edged with boxwood or domesticated flowers, espaliered fruit trees in rows, and turf squares bordered again with boxwood or flowers. In short, the gardens were everything the surrounding countryside was not.

What Alec and George saw as they strode out into that June morning had nothing to do with formality, with straight lines and mathematical precision, or with man-made beauty. Nature was at its best. The walls straggling up the hillsides were of rocks torn out of the mountains themselves, and they zigzagged up the slopes, following the contour of the land, deviating where a boulder was too large to be extracted, stopping altogether where a stream made an erratic bolt into the wall's path. Even the village of Grasmere, below, was laid out to conform with the shape of the hill, and there were no right angles in those streets. The houses nestled so naturally, they might have grown as spontaneously as lichen upon rocks.

It was a captivating scene, and even Alec was momentarily silenced as he and George strode down the hill toward the village and the lake beyond.

"It is special," Alec finally murmured. "When I rode through yesterday afternoon I was so bedeviled by the long ride, the fog and my encounter with your gal that I scarcely took in the sights."

"I knew you'd think so," George answered eagerly. "Shall I tell you something about the District? If you wouldn't be too bored."

"No, tell on. You know I admire facts like beautiful women. One can never know too many."

"Well, as you see the Grasmere valley runs north to south. The lake there is more than a mile long. And like many valley lakes it is very, very deep so the fishing is excellent. And swimming.

"Actually, the whole of the Lake District isn't very large. It all fits into a circle that isn't much more than thirty miles across. But what there is of it is packed. Into that relatively small space, squeeze about a dozen considerable-sized lakes and one hundred and eighty mountains." He stopped at an incredulous sniff from his listener. "They *are* mountains, Ali. By all definitions."

"I shan't dispute the terminology, but they aren't exactly Alps, are they?"

"Course not. A little over three thousand feet is the highest here."

"This is indeed pleasant, George."

Mollified, George continued his description. Though it was early June, the gentle summer weather that had come to Alec's estate in southern England had not appeared here in the north. There was a cold wind. The ash trees were coming into full leaf but the honeysuckles were still a thousand buds. And the oak tree leaves were dry and the oak copses still brown. Bypassing the village of whitewashed cottages, the men walked on down to the edge of the lake, where they sat.

"Hallo!" Alec whistled. "There, if I am not mistaken, is your friend." He squinted against the sun. "Just what is she up to now, I wonder?"

"Where? I don't see."

"There, across the lake."

"It is! Tish!" he shouted. "Here! It's me. It's me."

The girl, halfway around the other side of the lake, looked up at his shout and waved. Tossing something down, she began to run toward George as he also broke into a gallop.

Alec had never seen a girl run so. Free and unbound by restraints. He watched as she and George collided into each other's arms and hugged. They paused an unusually long time, it seemed to Alec, before they turned to walk back to him.

"You two have met," George beamed. "Tish, this is Alec Grenfell. Tish Abbott."

"M'lord," she said formally.

"Nonsense!" George interrupted. "We don't stand on titles here. You must call him by his name, as I do. And he must call you Tish."

She looked quizzically at Alec, judging his reaction. Feeling her critical eye, he wasn't about to be put at a disadvantage twice in two days.

"I should be grateful if you would use my Christian name and allow me the same privilege," he said easily.

"Of course she will. Won't you?" George urged.

"If you like," she said politely. The smile she turned on George was considerably warmer. "I am glad to see you. I had heard you were home, of course. I was coming to see you this afternoon."

"Not in that get-up, I trust," George teased.

"This?" she laughed. "Perhaps his lordship—sorry, perhaps Alexander would give us his opinion as to whether my present costume is appropriate for afternoon calls at Lansdale Hall. He is quite a connoisseur, I believe, of ladies' fashion."

Refusing to rise to the bait, Alec surveyed her without immediate comment. She was dressed as a country girl, clad in a neat dark-gray gown, thick-soled clogs, blue stockings, blue-checked apron, and a bright, cherry-colored neckerchief.

He cleared his throat judiciously. "You seem to have an affinity for baskets, ma'am. Yesterday you were in one, today when I first saw you you were carrying one." He noted with satisfaction that she was the one now to struggle with her temper. "Perhaps your costume today is suited to today's basket."

"You are very clever, m'lord," she admitted. "Indeed, I have been picking gooseberries." She frowned slightly. "Did you see me, then, before George?"

He only nodded, and they stared at each other for a full minute.

"Speaking of baskets," George interjected, "I want to hear about your adventure yesterday. Let's retrieve the gooseberries and find a sheltered spot to sit out of the wind."

Tish glanced up. "A cold south wind portends rain, you know, but I think it will hold off for a bit. Very well. But I warn you, George, you must not eat all the gooseberries or my family shall be without pie for their tea."

"Then you shall take tea with Alec and me," he smiled.

Sparring and joking with the familiarity of close friends, George and Tish led the way away from the lake, trailed by a pensive Alec.

After some discussion between Tish and George as to the direction their walk should take, it was determined to head for the hills to the east—a point known as Nab Scar. The pace set was brisk and did not falter when the grass gave way to stones and the ground began to slope upward. There were a few yew trees, grown grotesquely twisted in the wind, but for the most part the hillside was bare, offering only rocky perches. Several spots were proposed by George but Tish rejected them all, insisting they must push on for a more perfect resting place.

Like all his British countrymen, Alec enjoyed wagers. He would debate for hours the finer points of blood horses at Tattersall's or argue endlessly over the potential of heroes of the ring like Tom Cribb or Tom Hickman the Gas-light Man. For all that, he couldn't fathom the point of debating a picnic spot. What difference did it make? he fumed, as George and Tish wrangled enthusiastically over a choice bit of rock.

In exasperation he at last strode ahead, noting with dour satisfaction that the sharp pebbles were slicing into the butter-soft leather of his boots. Ruddick would have a fit! And he would have something to say to his valet about the appropriateness of such footwear for mountain climbing.

Scrambling over a large boulder, he stopped short. He had discovered a refuge from the wind and the flinty hillside. A high slab of rock to the side of the hill, higher than his head, was mantled with ivy. Outcrops of rock on both sides were hung with more ivy and spotted with tiny yellow and purple flowers, while moss made a carpet at his feet. With a tinge of pride and excitement, he called to the others.

There was just room in the bower for the three to stretch

out. Sheltered from the wind, they basked in the sun's warmth and lazily consumed the small, sour berries from Tish's basket.

"I think I shall come back here tomorrow and scatter seeds," Tish mused aloud. "Imagine how glorious it would look with a tangle of blooms there and there. Foxgloves or roses."

"I thought you preferred your scenery as nature arranged it?" George grinned. "And yet you aren't here ten minutes before you wish to alter things."

Tish grinned, too. "I don't fault nature but we are part of nature, too, so if we sprinkle a few seeds here and there or try to root a bush, I think it's all right."

"But this is Alec's find," George continued. "Haven't you to ask his permission?"

"Do you claim this spot, then?" she turned to Alec.

He felt unreasonably annoyed by their lighthearted banter. George's teasing elicited only good-natured replies from the girl. While his . . . "Tell me what all that is," he suggested, waving at the scene which lay at their feet.

"You evade the issue," Tish said with a tentative smile.

Alec smiled back and suddenly his mood changed. "I have not studied the terrain," he said lightly, "and therefore I will not lay any claims until I know all the options and consequences."

"You see the lessons he has learned from the military," George murmured.

"Quite right. All maneuvers are canceled until I become oriented."

"Oh yes," Tish said with an impish grin, "it would never do for you to become disoriented, m'lord. Let me help. That is Grasmere, of course. The lake with its green collar and then the bare ring of hills. And there is the river that runs out of the lake. There, to the southwest, Coniston Fells."

"Fells?"

"Hills. And there, south of Grasmere vale, is Rydal vale

with its wee lake. And there, beyond, Ambleside lake and village. It is larger than Grasmere."

"Almost anything is," George muttered.

"One can't see that far," Tish continued, "but if you could see farther south you would find Windermere Lake. That's the largest lake of all, in fact, the largest lake in all England. The queen lake. And farther south and a bit east is Kendal. You came that way. We often walk to Kendal for our mail."

"And the highest mountain?" Alec prompted.

"Helvellyn. It's over three thousand feet," Tish said proudly.

"A Norse name?"

"Of course. Most of the names here are Norse. Helvellyn is to the north of Grasmere. From the top on a clear day you can see almost all the District mountains, and even on to Scotland and the Irish Sea." Her eyes glowed and her cheeks, whipped red by the chill wind on the climb, flamed even more brightly.

"When I'm atop Helvellyn, and I go there often, I think what it must be like floating over them all. Seeing the clear lakes far below like splashes of color—blue or silver or gray, depending on the sky above. Imagine encompassing the whole beauty of it all in one view . . ." she said dreamily, "as if one could stretch out one's arms and embrace it. Experience it all as a bird must. . . ."

"You mean as one in a balloon must!" Alec ventured impulsively.

Tish blinked, as though awakened too suddenly. "I was not thinking of a balloon," she said mutinously.

"Don't fly up into the boughs, old girl," George soothed. "Though perhaps under the circumstances I should find a better expression!" He was pleased to see her relent a trifle at his small pun. "Do tell us about the balloon, Tish. I am sincerely interested. And so is Alec."

She glared at Alec and then sighed. "For you, George. Though there's really nothing much to tell. Grand-père and I are trying out the balloon. Yesterday was our first real trial. It has taken us weeks to rig up a mechanism for filling the sac."

"Where on earth did you get such a thing?" George asked.

"Grand-père bought it, long ago. He took many balloon trips in France, but he had to leave it behind when he came to England. It was only now that he was able to send for it— since the war ended, you see, and mail is exchanged so much more easily."

"You said your grandfather is too incapacitated to go up in the thing himself?" Alec couldn't resist reminding her.

"He has crippling arthritis," she flashed.

"And he considers it wise that you substitute for him?" Alec insisted.

"Yes!" She jumped to her feet and glowered down at him.

"And your mother?"

Her sparkling brown eyes widened. "My mother . . . has made no objections."

"And after your mishap yesterday, when you might have been seriously hurt, or killed, has your grandfather abandoned notions of future flights?" Alec was relentless.

"We shall certainly not abandon our plans. You may be assured that we shall not have such a mishap again."

"And just how are your bruises and scratches today?" he shot at her, also jumping to his feet so that he once again towered over her.

"Fine! I am not so fragile," she said contemptuously.

"You have no business banging about in that contraption."

"That, my lord, is none of *your* business."

"He's right, you know, Tish," George said thoughtfully, regarding them both. "Females are just too delicate to be racketing around in the sky."

"Nonsense," she said witheringly.

"It ain't right," he persisted. "Females don't belong in such risky adventures."

"George, females have been ballooning practically since the things were invented."

"Don't try to gammon me, my girl," George smiled.

"But it's true," she said exasperatedly. "The first flight was in November 1783, in France, with a hot-air balloon. A few days later, Professor Charles went up in a gas-filled balloon. And," she crowed, "it was only a few months later, in June, that an opera singer named Madame Thible became the first woman aeronaut. It was in Lyons, and she was so far from being prostrate with fear that she took inspiration from the exhilarating experience and sang an aria as she floated through the clouds. Lots of women have become aeronauts since then!"

"I admit that few inventions have ever caught the public's fancy as has the balloon," Alec frowned, "but why is it necessary for you to become an aeronaut?"

"I must." She almost whispered. "That's all. I must."

George shook his head dubiously. "I don't see it, Tish. I really don't. You told Ardenly here that it is none of his business and I concede the truth of that. But will you say the same to me?"

"Of course not," she said quickly. "We are old friends."

"It worries me."

"Please, don't worry. There will be no more accidents. I'm sure."

"Then how did the rope break, the one that was supposed to hold the balloon down?" George asked.

"It was old. Perhaps it had been stored where it was damp. We cannot know. It has to be replaced."

George's expression of worry did not lighten, but he let the subject drop.

Scooping up a handful of ivy and flowers, Tish sprinkled them on George's head. "Perhaps it is all destiny," she joked, trying to coax an answering smile. "George, did I ever tell you how I was named?"

"Nope."

"Letitia Sage." She flashed Alec a mocking grin. "When Grand-père heard Mama was to have a child, he wrote and

asked that if it were a girl, she should be named after Letitia
Sage."

"And who the blazes is she?" Alec muttered between
clenched jaws.

Tish dimpled prettily. "Why, she is an aeronaut, naturally.
She was the first Englishwoman to go up in a balloon—June
twenty-ninth, 1785. Ah, it's almost her anniversary! And you
would have approved of her garb, Lord Ardenly. She wore an
elegant gown and jacket and a fancy plumed hat." She
laughed, delighted to see George smiling slightly.

"Now that I think of it, Letitia had a mishap with her first
flight also. In fact, she nearly received her *congé* before rising
as much as a foot into the air." She paused dramatically.
"Alas, the lady was stout and added too much weight to the
passengers. Fortunately, one of the two gentlemen in the basket with her was a kind man and he stepped out. Where-
upon, Letitia went up!"

Scrambling nimbly over the rocks, she disappeared down
the hillside without a farewell.

CHAPTER 4

The Dowager Marchioness Lady Margaret glided into the salon like a dark shadow, insubstantial yet dampening to the spirits. She was short, slight, and gowned in black silk with a black lace scarf over her head which was fluttery, yet noiseless as she moved. Alec felt himself a giant beside her, and he took her alabaster-white hand with gingerly care as he made his bow.

"You must forgive me for not receiving you before. I was abed with a fearsome cold. Good evening, George." Her voice was so low-pitched and quiet that one had to strain to catch her words. She brushed her son's cheek with a feathery kiss before perching on the edge of a gilt chair.

"How long have you been here, Ardenly?" she whispered.

Alec shook his head slightly; he hadn't quite heard the question.

"He's been here a week, Mama," George replied in his stead.

"Tell me, what have you two been doing to amuse yourselves?"

Again George had to answer and Alec shifted uncomfortably in his chair. This was going to be a deucedly awkward visit if he could never hear his hostess!

"We've been fishing, ma'am," George was saying. "We've been doing a great deal of fishing. The time has passed most agreeably."

Before he could miss another round of questions, Alec pulled his chair closer to the Dowager Marchioness' side. By leaning almost against her shoulder, he was able to respond to her next query.

"Tell me, Lord Ardenly, what do you think of our home here in the remote isolation of the north?"

"Not so remote, Lady Margaret, now that the romance of the lakes is extolled by so many travel writers. And your home is as gracious and welcoming as any in London."

"Thank you." She turned to look directly at him for the first time and her face was exposed, just for a second, to the full strength of the light from the candles on the mantel-piece. There remained not a single vestige of her once-famous beauty. She had the defeated, worn look of a person who has barely survived a long illness. Then she adjusted the veil more closely around her face and Alec was left, again, to try to decipher her words without the clue of her expression.

"We are indeed less remote than we once were," she said in a breathy, low voice. "When I was a child it was an occasion of wonder to see a carriage of any sort on the road. And we scarcely had a visitor from one season to the next. It was even more lonely than now."

"Yet you chose to live here, ma'am," Alec said reasonably.

"Do you know Dorset, sir? Where my dear husband, the late Lord Lansdale, lived?"

"I have visited there, though not for long."

"I do not wonder if your stays were not extended. Pray do not misunderstand. When my dearest husband was alive there was no spot on earth more desirable than our home in Dorset. Our time together was brief but every moment perfection!" She said this emphatically, her voice almost raised to a normal level. "However, after his untimely death I emerged from the sorrow of mourning to discover that I couldn't breathe in that dull, stodgy atmosphere. When he lived, all was enchantment. Afterward, it all was flat!" She put a wealth of loathing into that last word.

"Don't upset yourself, Mama."

"You were an infant, George. How could you know? I was expected to pass my days in a series of duty calls on the local society who spoke of nothing but their offspring, their symptoms, and their gowns. And as if that weren't enough, I was expected to assume the role of Lady of the Hall. To drive to the wretched cottages where the workers lived and dispense bottles of tonic or baskets of fruit. As if that would cure their ills or lighten their lives!"

"Mother!" George warned. "You are becoming overexcited. Let us speak of something more congenial. I understand we are to have company for dinner."

"Yes, change the subject," she said pettishly. "But it wasn't fair. I thought George's father was going to take me to live in London and yet we were there just three weeks, on our honeymoon. I was quite admired, if you will allow me to brag a bit, Lord Ardenly. But it is the truth. I was feted and toasted. . . . And my gowns . . ." She sat even straighter. "And then his father died suddenly and we had to return to Dorset. Just to straighten out the estate, he said. And just as unexpectedly I discovered that we were to increase our family. And I hadn't even begun to know London. But all the old aunts and cousins persuaded him I should need the country air in my condition. After the birth we should return to London, he said. He promised. Only, I had barely delivered when he took a jump too recklessly and broke his neck. It was over. I have been in poor health since. I never had a strong constitution, and to suffer such a shock . . ." she concluded disconsolately.

George drummed impatiently on his knee as he contemplated his mother, but he made no further try to stop her recital. It was as if he knew she had to say a set piece, and could not halt halfway through.

"You may ask why I did not go to London by myself," she said querulously, throwing back the scarf and exposing her ravaged features without compunction. "You must understand that I was just eighteen. I could not, would not, go alone. So I remained in Dorset with the weight of the family. Oh, the family! I waited hours for dinner to end only to face hours in the drawing room with the dull aunts and cousins and even more stupid men!

"They said I couldn't leave. I couldn't take George away from his birthright. But I found a way. I gave him his birthright here—the same house. Only, here." Her eyes were feverishly bright, her cheeks flushed.

The monologue was interrupted by the entrance of the head butler. "The Honorable Hugh Woffington and Lady Olivia Woffington," he intoned.

"My George has been my comfort," Lady Margaret hissed to Alec as she drew the protective veil close again. "He has been my all."

The couple advancing into the drawing room were obviously brother and sister, for they shared the same strikingly good looks. Though in their early twenties, both had prematurely white hair that contrasted dramatically with dark brown, almost black eyes. Both were tall and dressed in the latest style.

To Alec's amazement, Lady Margaret was completely composed in her greeting. The *sotto voce* whispers, the hysterical harangue might never have happened.

As Woffington explained, he and his sister were touring the Lake District. Friends in Dorset had sent Lady Margaret a letter of introduction which she had received the day before. He thanked her for her alacrity in inviting them to Lansdale Hall.

"You live in Dorset, Mr. Woffington?" Lady Margaret asked sharply.

"My family home is there, ma'am, and my parents prefer the country so they remain in Dorset most of the year. My sister and I are more partial to London and we keep the house there open. Naturally, we travel down to Dorset frequently to pay our respects to our parents." His voice was as handsome as his countenance, not particularly deep but intimate, as though he were confiding a secret to the listener.

"And what brings you to our lakes?" Lady Margaret turned dutifully to his sister.

"I heard a talk, Lady Margaret, by a Mr. Horne, a gentleman who traveled much in this area. He had done magnificent drawings which he used to illustrate his talk. It was so fascinating that I went straightaway and purchased his book on the lakes of Lancashire, Westmorland and Cumberland." Her manner and voice were also charming and confiding. She smiled fondly at her brother.

"Hugh and I are the tail end of a large family. Being considerably younger than our brothers and sisters, we are used to each other's company. So when I resolved to visit this enchanted land, I conspired to have Hugh with me."

"And did that require great persuasion?" Lady Margaret asked archly.

"I should come readily on a second visit, now that I have seen the country," Hugh replied diplomatically. "It is all that the wise Mr. Horne claimed. But I confess that, being ignorant before of the attractions here, it did require considerable persuasion to bring me to reside in a country inn."

"Fortunately for my interests," Olivia smiled, "all of Hugh's cronies desert London by mid-June. The weather is frightful hot, as you know, ma'am, and the society quite dead."

"Of course. Though it has been some years since I was in London."

Anticipating that this might trigger a repeat of his mother's earlier grievances, George spoke up.

"And where are you stopping, Woffington?"

"We're at the White Lion Inn in Ambleside. Very comfortable, really. Convenient to all the walks. Excellent food."

"It was recommended by Mr. Horne," Olivia explained. "He said, I believe, that it is 'singularly clean and inviting.'

And he was correct in both. And it also boasts a superb view of Windermere Lake from the front lawn. Perhaps you would do us the honor of taking tea with us there someday soon, Lady Margaret?" A smile included the gentlemen in the invitation.

"I do not go out." Her voice was flat.

"Alec and I would be delighted," George put in quickly. "I must keep him busy lest he grow bored with our rustic life, and Windermere is certainly worth a visit."

Alec stifled a chuckle. The son could be as wanting in tact as his mother. "I should be glad to see the queen of the lakes under any circumstances," he said smoothly, "but in your company it will be a special pleasure, Miss Woffington."

Olivia's answering smile was warm. "There is a ferry on the lake and an island. Perhaps we might make a picnic."

"Excellent plan," her brother agreed. "Just the scheme for a pleasant day."

Just then a footman announced dinner and the party rose.

One hundred years earlier, Lord Lansdale's great-grandfather had been smitten by the rebuilding craze that was then sweeping England. The result was a Georgian façade, portico and wings, tacked onto the Tudor core of Lansdale Hall in Dorset. The exterior was in the Palladian style, which meant a measured use of Corinthian columns, marble statuary, and porticoes. The interior, also according to Palladian rules, was remodeled so that old oak paneling gave way to plaster walls with painted-on moldings, and doors and fireplaces were embellished with more columns and entablatures. All this was simply imposed upon the existing Tudor confusion of rambling corridors and odd staircases.

Lansdale Hall in Grasmere improved upon the original in that the interior was as ordered as the facade. The drawing room to the right of the antechamber was matched by a dining room on the left. Twin courts led from these chambers to a series of equally elaborate and symmetrical rooms: an enormous library matched by a vast conservatory; billiard room and breakfast room; music room and bedroom—the latter for those guests who found it difficult after a long evening to ascend a staircase to the guest bedchambers on the second floor. Columns graduated from Doric to Ionic to Corinthian orders and marbles changed from white to black to green to rose, but everywhere was the classical style so admired in Georgian England.

It struck Alec, as he escorted Lady Margaret in to dinner, that his hostess was more suited to the style of architecture currently in vogue than to the Georgian. For the present taste was for romantic Gothic, with carefully constructed ruins, heavy wood carvings, and asymmetrical floor plans. She was too theatrical for this chaste, spare setting. But it was all for George, he reminded himself ruefully. George was her "all."

What did suit Lady Margaret as queen bee of her private world was the retinue of seventy servants who moved soundlessly in dark-gray livery through the Hall, replacing enormous arrangements of flowers almost before the blooms had opened fully, restocking the fires so that they never burned less than brightly, and answering the bell-pull before the second ring had sounded. In fact, one seldom had to resort to the bell-pull, for wishes were assiduously anticipated. Blank-faced young footmen in powdered hair and drab gray whisked open doors as the party proceeded to the dining room; identically anonymous men pulled back chairs and seated the guests; others—or perhaps they were the same footmen—stationed themselves behind each chair during dinner; and still others appeared and deftly presented silver platters of fish and joints of meat and sweet trifles. The guests, as was polite, paid the servants no attention but gave the excellent food the concentration its high quality deserved.

The Dowager Marchioness attempted to orchestrate the conversation from the end of the long mahogany table. Her voice was, by now, quite audible. Apparently she simply needed a sort of tune-up time. She exhibited a wide knowledge of business and politics and peppered Alec and Hugh

Woffington with questions about the state of affairs and climate of opinion in London.

"I amuse myself in my solitude," she explained, "by devouring newspapers and journals. Thus I am not entirely alienated from the world. They make the political scene so vivid that it is as though I am in the House of Commons gallery, listening to speeches and applauding or booing with the members. Do you follow politics, Mr. Woffington?"

"I fear not, ma'am. It is dry stuff for my head." He excused himself with a sweet smile. "Happily there are three sons between the old Earl, my father, and me so that there is no likelihood of me inheriting the title. I would not care overmuch for the duties that go with the honor. Nevertheless I am all admiration for those gentlemen who set the course of our great barque and I rely on their wisdom to do what is best."

"And you, Lord Ardenly, have you the same faith in our leaders?" quizzed Lady Margaret.

"I wish I had," he said with a shrug. "Perhaps it is evidence of my greater age, though I cannot recall that I was ever less cynical than I am now, ma'am. I cannot place blind trust in any man, and I suspect that the view a leader gets from his vantage ground is as limited as that of the stableboy from his more humble place."

"And what do you foresee?" his hostess continued. "What is that course that Mr. Woffington mentioned? Where does it lead us?"

"To troubled waters, ma'am. To use his metaphor. I do not like to say so but I have no doubt in my mind. Just look what has happened. We have prospered from our war economy. But daily thousands of soldiers and sailors are being discharged and they have no jobs to return to. Wages are low, yet import duties are high so that many cannot buy what they need. The price farmers got for wheat during wartime is impossible to sustain in peace. I could go on and on.

"In some quarters, Boney may be missed," he concluded laconically.

"You are pessimistic, sir," Olivia Woffington said gravely. "Yet surely the battles we have won are proof that we can conquer the problems you cite."

Darting a glance at Lady Margaret, Alec was alarmed to see that she was listening with a hectic excitement and that George was gulping his wine and seemed distracted, not about to intervene.

"I'm sure we shall overcome those problems, as you suggest," Alec said pleasantly. "And they are, in any case, remote from us tonight. Happily remote. For the moment, I am intrigued by your allusion to Mr. Horne, Miss Woffington. Please tell us more of his lecture."

Under his prompting, Olivia repeated almost verbatim the esteemed Mr. Horne's discourse on the Lake country, and Alec was gratified to note that Lady Lansdale grew visibly less agitated under the soothing drone of the young lady's mellifluous tones. Her brother, seemingly hardened through years of familiarity with her pedantry, applied himself enthusiastically to his dinner, nodding from time to time when called upon to verify some claim or other. Lord Lansdale, too well-mannered to do anything else, listened with apparent rapt attention and drank vast quantities of wine. And Lord Ardenly, relieved to see the tension at the table abate, allowed his mind to wander. He honestly did believe that England's postwar problems would be solved eventually, but he was also convinced that there would be grave crises in the immediate future. For some reason, that gloomy thought reminded him of a canal-building scheme that interested him. He had invested a fair bit, but he could afford far more. He was recalled to the present by a discreet poke in the ribs. Hugh Woffington, at his side, was giving him a friendly dig with his elbow.

"I was asking, Lord Ardenly, if you had visited the museum in Kendal?" Miss Woffington was saying.

"Alec only passed through Kendal," George offered help-fully. "He did not have an opportunity to visit Todhunter's Museum."

Alec nodded. "Only passed through," he echoed.

"Then perhaps we can all make an excursion there another day," Olivia proposed happily. "It is well worth the visit, I promise. There are specimens of vegetables and minerals typi-cal of the Cumberland and Westmorland counties. Also a considerable variety of seashells."

"Fascinating," Alec said dutifully. Catching a glimpse of George's expression, he fought to control his features. Who would save them from this new discourse on vegetables and minerals? The Dowager Marchioness, he saw, was now snoring softly, her tiny figure sagging gracefully against the back of her chair. And damned if he knew how to extricate himself! But he should have known better than to worry. In this house everything was handled by the servants. Every-thing. At just that moment, the butler announced in a sten-torian tone that awoke the sleeping hostess, "Coffee and tea are served in the drawing room, my lady." At once awake and smiling affably, Lady Lansdale arose in a flutter of black silk and lace and led Olivia Woffington from the room—leav-ing the men to fall upon the crystal decanter of French brandy with unusual zeal.

CHAPTER 5

There was an uncomfortable silence. The angular old woman pulled the brush ferociously through Tish's long hair again and again.

"There! That's two hundred. You can get up now."

Instead, Tish turned and put her arms around the old woman's waist, burying her face in the white cotton apron that she wore. "It will be all right, Nanny. I know it will."

The rough hands were gentle as down as they patted her head. "I'm not sure, child. That balloon half worries me to death. And it's useless to talk to your grandfather. He just sits in that funny chair reading his books or staring at the sky and scribbling notes as if there were messages in the clouds! But go on, now. Put your dress on or you'll catch yourself a chill. The sun ain't barely shown itself yet and the air is cold." She frowned. "You've smudges as black as ink under your eyes. Were you troubled in your sleep?"

"Something disturbed me," Tish confessed. "I thought it was Mama, yet I crept a half-dozen times and listened at her door without hearing anything out of the ordinary."

Nanny bristled. "You know I'm right in the next room to her. I'm there to tend to her at night."

"I know. But I awoke in the middle of the night and felt so—so uneasy. And Grand-père was sleeping soundly. I peeked into his room. I didn't know where else to look."

" 'Tisn't right that you be all solitary, searching out trouble," Nanny sighed. "Nor that you be alone in this house, defenseless, save for your grandfather and your poor mother and me. Your mother is still ill, poor soul. I can't think what your father was about, going off that way—deserting you, as it were."

"Don't!" Tish shuddered. "Don't speak of him in that way. Please, Nanny."

"Never mind. Never mind," the old woman soothed. "We can't have servants sleeping here, I know that. It's just that I don't relish the thought of you worrying and fretting in the dark of night and no one to turn to."

"How can you say that!" Tish replied indignantly. "I have Grand-père. And I have you."

"Yes, you have me," the old woman agreed. "And always shall. But you know as well as I that I'm not the proper companion for a young lady. I was just an upstairs maid when your father left. It fair to broke my heart, you were such a scrawny, sad chick. Almost taller than me, even then, but a child for all that. I had to step in, had to try my hand at caring for you."

"You may not be a proper nanny," Tish grinned, "but it was you who got Grand-père to send me to that dreadful girls' school in Bath."

"And a good thing too, or you wouldn't know none of the fine lady things, like drawing and music. I don't know about those things myself, but I know what's right!"

"And look how well I've turned out between Grand-père and you and Miss Webb's School for Young Ladies," Tish grinned. "But I'm not a child now," she went on more seriously. "I'm a grown woman, Nanny. And you and Grand-père have done too good a job of making me feel independent to try and convince me now that we are defenseless just because we haven't a strong male in the house."

"Yes, you're the age of a woman, but it isn't age alone that makes a female womanly!"

Tish giggled. "Now don't start nagging about my spinster state or I vow I shall put on a cap and publicly declare myself on the shelf."

"You're no such thing," Nanny said, horrified.

"Perhaps not. But I am three and twenty and I am not afraid to walk through my own house at night. I have a pistol, after all. And I shoot as straight as any man."

"Stuff and nonsense," Nanny clucked. "Your grandfather has more strange notions than any man I know. Teaching you to shoot, indeed! Sometimes I'm not sure who has less brains, him or your poor mama."

"Nanny!" Tish warned.

"I'll be quiet. But it wasn't me was scared in the night and looks like a ghost this morning." Grumbling under her breath, the old woman went to tidy the bed.

"I'll do that," the girl protested as she pulled on her dress.

"You have enough to do," the woman answered angrily. "Too much, to my way of thinking."

The bedchamber was minuscule, holding only a small bed more like a cot, a washstand, and a single stool. The walls, whitewashed over rough plaster, were bare of ornament. One tiny window, set high, showed the pink of a clear, cloudless dawn.

The woman stumbled against a stack of books buried on the floor under the tumbled blanket and coverlet.

"While you weren't roaming, you were reading, I suppose," she snapped. "And with one candle. Ruin your eyes, you will, with all that reading in the dark. And what is it now? More of that history, I'll wager." She regarded the stack of books suspiciously.

Apparently accidentally, Tish used her toe to nudge the volumes farther under the bed, but her nanny knew her too well for that.

"What are you reading, miss? Shall I carry them books to your grandfather?"

"No, Nanny," Tish blushed. "They're just novels."

"Novels?"

"I happened to meet Miss Follett yesterday. She had received a parcel of books from the lending library. And she lent me a couple."

"The parson's daughter reads novels!" Nanny exclaimed.

"Everyone does," Tish said defensively.

"You don't."

"Well, I thought I would try one. Just to see what they are. After all, you and Grand-père always taught me not to judge without knowledge. Anyway, they are harmless. Just little stories."

The old woman's face softened. "And you be caring to read some stories now instead of those histories about battles and such?"

Tish shrugged. "Just for a change." She gave the woman a hug and kiss. "It's too nice to stay in a moment longer."

She was gone like a whirlwind, but the old woman didn't budge. She remained staring at the floor, her head wagging, her expression grim, until footsteps in the hallway recalled her to her duties.

The house where Tish and her grandfather lived was a squat old farmhouse much like the others in the Grasmere vale. The walls, whitewashed inside and out, were three feet thick, of local stone, and the gray slate of the roof also came from neighboring quarries. Like a number of farmhouses in the District, it was grafted onto a peel tower, a massive refuge against Scottish raiders during the Border troubles centuries earlier. The tower was sturdy, square and not too tall, so as to avoid notice from afar.

Back of the house was a scattering of tumbled-down farm buildings, including a rather substantial barn. Because of the dampness of the region, cereal crops were often harvested damp. Therefore the barns provided a means of drying the hay. The typical barn was built on the natural steep slope of a hill with the downward side entrance leading to the cow house and stable. The upward side had a ramp and the hay was kept there. The upper floor of the drying chamber consisted of slate slabs with spaces between, to allow the warm air to circulate. The air came from a heating chamber below.

To all appearances, the outside of the barn Tish entered now followed the norm. The difference was on the inside, because the upper floor was filled with the sagging, half-collapsed yellow-and-blue sac. And the heating chamber on the lower level had been altered by the addition of several pipes and a large furnace.

"Good morning, Bowen," Tish cried out. She had grabbed a large chunk of bread and an apple as she ran through the kitchen and she was nibbling at them both. At the doorway, momentarily blinded at the abrupt change from the early morning sun to the darkness of the barn, she halted.

"'Tain't so good a day as you might expect, miss," the farmer replied. He was bent over the heating machinery.

"Why, what's the matter? Has Grand-père been in?"

"He's still abed, miss. Message from the house was that he is feeling poorly. I was to get on with filling the balloon. But I cannot."

The girl dropped the last crust into her pocket and crossed to his side. She peered at the jumble of pipes.

"See there?" the old man grunted. "Pipe burst clean in two. Must've got so hot it split in half." The farmer stepped back and wiped his hands on a rag. "All I know is that it took weeks to put the works together. Now it's ruint. Completely."

Tish stared numbly at the wreckage. "It cannot be," she said slowly. "Grand-père will be heartbroken. And I was counting on it. I have to make another flight. And soon!"

"But where are we to get another part like that one but stronger? Look, miss," the man said reasonably, "I promised I was in the game with you and your grandpa and I don't go back on my word. But I know when I'm licked. Better turn your thoughts to something else. Without the proper tubes to feed the gas from the iron filings to the sac there, there ain't no way to inflate the thing. And that's that." He tossed the rag into a corner. "I must attend to the animals." He nodded gravely. "Don't fret, miss. 'Twas a daft idea. You know that." Then he was gone.

Why had it happened? Tish raged silently. Everything has to be hard, it seems. Why can't things go easily, just once?

It was hopeless as it was, that was sure. She kept turning the problem over in her mind, round and round without solution, trying to operate the chamber without the faulty tube. Impossible. She simply had to replace it before her grandfather was well enough to come and see the project for himself. She glanced down at her homespun apron. Nanny would have a hysterical fit if she went again to Kendal in this garb. Impatiently she ran back to the house to change.

She was concealed by the thick branches overhanging the narrow path, and it was only at the last split second that the rider saw her and, pulling sharply on the bridle, swerved to bring his trembling mount to a halt.

"You are a menace," Alec snarled angrily, jumping out of the saddle and seizing her by the wrist. "Do you mean to kill us both or just me?"

Tish was shaken too by the near-miss, and to her shame her eyes filled with tears. "It is you who are a menace," she charged in a wavery voice. "I was nearly run down by that— that black beast."

"That beast, ma'am, is better trained than you," Alec snapped. "If he hears something in his path he moves aside. Did it not occur to you to do the same?"

It was impossible to hold back all the tears and two or three traitorous drops rolled down Tish's cheeks. "You frightened me," she said defensively, trying without success to pull her wrist free.

His scowl deepened at the sight of the tears. "Damn and hell's fire," he raged. "I could have broken my neck just now and yet you make it clear that I am expected to apologize. You are beyond reason!"

"I did not say you were to apologize," she sniffled, "though you should."

"You do not have to say anything," he replied darkly. "When a female turns on the waterworks, reasonable conversation flies out the window."

"You are anything but reasonable!" she charged.

"Could you at least tell me why you did not move out of the path?" he shouted.

"I did not hear you before, though I certainly hear you well enough now. You needn't bellow!"

"Tarquin is a miraculous animal, ma'am, but he don't walk on air," Alec retorted.

"I was thinking," she snapped. "In any case, you have no right to hurtle down the mountain like a cavalry charge. These paths aren't suited for such speed."

"In that I will concur," he agreed grudgingly. He wished she would stop staring at the ground; he wanted to know if the tears were gone from her eyes.

"Tarquin hadn't had a good run in days and I gave him his head. I confess that was an error." He released her wrist.

"I will confess a fault, too," she said haltingly. "I was walking with my head in the clouds. And I shouldn't. But I have a problem. And I couldn't help but think on it."

"Can I help?" The words were out before he considered them, and the surprised look on Tish's face was no less apparent than that on his own.

"Thank you, but I shall work it out. I have to."

"The offer is a standing one." He was relieved to see no tears. In fact, she seemed composed. A thrush overhead trilled its distinctive notes.

"I wish you a good day, then." She felt shy under his intent scrutiny but she forced herself not to look away. She despised coquettish airs.

"Yes, all right," he answered slowly. He was almost bemused by the thrush's song and the green day. "Perhaps, if you've no objection, I'll accompany you a bit on your walk."

"Of course." She hesitated. "But I go fast. I'm on my way to Kendal, so I cannot delay."

"I shall do my best to match your pace," he said with mock gravity. And they both laughed.

"Haven't you to take Tarquin's reins?" she looked back.

"Oh no, he'll follow."

"Then he is far better trained than I," she laughed softly, "for I am a very poor follower."

He laughed too, and the look he gave her was so searching that she quickened her step even more to escape it and changed the subject.

"There are few diversions here," she ventured. "How is it that you have not had time to exercise your horse?"

"I have fallen in with George's mania," he joked. "We have each committed our honor to the catching of the largest, finest fish these lakes conceal. That pursuit requires arising almost before dawn so that we might snare the fellows before the sun reveals our presence. It also requires endless hours spent motionless in a rowboat, studying the translucent blue waters, speculating on the merits of one bait versus another, the advantages of a windy day versus a still one, the taste of perch versus pike. And so on. But then you must appreciate our single-mindedness, for George tells me that you are a fine fisherman yourself."

"Shall I share a long-kept secret?" she said impulsively.

"Please."

"I do not care so much for the fishing itself as for the excuse it offers to be out of doors with good company." She giggled at his exaggerated gasp of shock.

"And poor George," he moaned, "all these years has thought you bent solely on snaring fish. I've said it before, females aren't to be reasoned with: they make fools of us all."

"Not fools," she protested. "George is not a fool. I do like catching the fish, truly and eating them, of course. But George is able to concentrate on the catching for hours, as you say. Thinking of nothing else, while my mind wanders.

My attention is snagged, like the fish. Only the bait is the dappling of the sun on the water or the bursts of flowers on the shore." She laughed mischievously. "I should catch little, but I am blessed with the most phenomenal luck. Too often I must ignore a tug on my line. If I did not ignore them sometimes, I should be constantly pulling in fish, rebaiting the hook, pulling in fish again. There would be no chance at all to enjoy the scenery!"

He groaned again. "What woes! I repeat, poor George. But lucky me to be advised of your artful tricks. I shall not challenge you to a fishing contest, milady. We shall have to do contest in another field." His tone was suddenly serious and he looked away.

The few days of warm weather since his arrival had brought more signs of summer. The coppices were no longer brown and the hawthorn blossoms on the lower hillsides had passed, while those on the hilltops were now having their turn at painting the vista faint white. Wild roses were coming out and the first ripe strawberries and foxgloves had appeared.

"Do you walk all the sixteen miles to Kendal? And then back?"

"It doesn't seem long," she assured him. "I'll be there by lunchtime. And home again for tea."

"Then you won't be out after dark?"

She smiled and shook her head. "I shall be home before dark tonight, sir, but the fact is that I am often out after dark. I know these hills. Every twist and turn."

"Yet you did not know the refuge I discovered on Nab Scar," he reminded her.

"Almost every twist and turn," she amended. "And we are not so bound by clocks as you London folks, so that one must dine when it is the hour for dining and go to bed at another certain hour. Why, sometimes I set off after dinner and walk as far as Kendal to post a letter. The moon serves as guide as well as the sun."

"If it shines," he replied with asperity. "Which it frequently does not, owing to rain and fog and mist. What then?"

"Why, then I find me a hogg's hole," she bantered, "and I wait for the moon to reappear. Or I keep on walking. I do not melt with a little dampness."

"Hogg's hole?"

"The hole in the wall left so that sheep can pass through," she laughed.

"You make it sound snug," he conceded, "but I would rather travel a storm in a closed carriage."

"But then, you would rather be astride that great black beauty than be walking!"

He gave her a considering look. "Most of the time, yes, I would."

"And I would rather be afoot," she said simply.

"And aside from the fact that these hills have no roads fit for horses or carriages, why do you prefer to walk?"

"Because I can feel and see nature better," she said instantly. "You ride above it all, too fast to see the small and humble details."

"And even at your phenomenally fast walking pace, which you suspected I could not equal, you see the details?" he quizzed her.

She smiled happily. "As I said, we do not live by clocks here. I take time to look about, to sit and study the beauties around me. I take strength and comfort from these hills and lakes. Nature teaches great truths."

His answering smile was distinctly cynical. "I told George that I admire the District and I also told him that I thought it nature in miniature. It is also nature at its best. The towering mountains of the Alps with their bottomless crevices and ice and wind are not so benign. And the lashing storms of the oceans are equally foreign to these placid lakes. I find nature too often destructive and terrible. I am not comforted by what I have seen at sea. Or by the avalanche I witnessed that took half a dozen lives as easily as you might stamp out an insect."

"You don't understand," she disagreed. "This is not a make-believe fairyland. You see it now at its most gentle season, when the rains are mild and the chill of the nights invigorating. The winters are another story, I assure you. It is not uncommon for us to become confused in the rage of a storm, even those of us who know these paths well. And every year one or two are frozen to death for losing their way. In these climes, survival is the aim."

"If what you say is so, and I agree that it is, then how does nature teach you anything except that she is vengeful and destructive?"

They had reached an overlook. Below was the vale of Kendal, the market town stretching out along the small lake. Absorbed in their talk, they halted and faced each other.

"Don't you see, men have made such a muddle of things?" In her intensity, Tish's voice shook and her cheeks flamed. "Grand-père has told me of the revolution in France and what followed. He was an idealist, and what happened?" she asked scornfully. "Men turned on one another and the bloodbath that followed had nothing to do with ideals.

"I saw man's inhumanity to man for myself in London. I could not believe the squalor, the brutality of life for most of the people. One could not avoid it except by traveling blindfold! What contrasts," she grimaced. "Elaborate, elegant evening parties in a country whose favorite national spectacles are public hangings!"

"Then we come to the same conclusion," Alec said thoughtfully. "For the carnage and waste of the battlefield resulted in my disillusionment with human nature also. I enlisted to help my country. I had received so much through the accident of birth, I felt I had a debt to pay. And the country was saved—but at a terrible cost, and all because of Bonaparte's evil ambitions and the machinations of merchants and politicians on both sides of the Channel who found that war fostered commerce."

"Then don't you realize there is solace and healing in nature?" Tish asked. "There is harmony here, truly there is. And in this simple life and simple people, one can find moral and spiritual truths more clearly than in the sophisticated world!"

"I wish I could believe it, but why should that be?" he asked softly, capturing her eyes with his.

"Perhaps because simple people do not have the distractions of the sophisticated, perhaps because they have a greater sense of the wholeness of life. Their purposes have a harmony. They sow their seeds and harvest the grain, the lambs are birthed, the wool sheared, the sheep sent to winter pastures. The rhythm is clear. The role of the people is clear. And they are loyal and unselfish, perhaps because it is clear that it benefits them all to be so."

"And the value of rational thinking, of logic?"

"Where has it led us?" she sighed. "To violence. Carnage, as you said. Brutal poverty for most."

"I cannot abandon my reverence for logic," he mused.

"We are different in many ways," she agreed.

"And yet our conversation strikes sparks, young Tish." He took a step toward her.

She flushed and moved aside. "Do you call me 'young' to remind yourself of another difference between us? Yet, I am long out of the schoolroom."

"I have ten years on you," he said dryly, "but it is your naïveté that makes me feel so decrepit." There was a soft caress to his voice and a gleam deep in his eyes that alarmed her.

"I am three and twenty," she said sharply.

"I know," he drawled. He openly studied her plain white muslin frock. It was cut in the classical fashion that had been popular in England for a decade, pulled tight under the bust with a ribbon and the skirt narrow. She carried a straw bonnet by its yellow ribbons, and a woolly yellow shawl was draped over one arm.

The light in his eyes grew stronger, and muttering, "Damn you, Tish, for looking that way," he reached out and drew her into his arms for the second time. His kiss was urgent and his embrace so unyielding that she could not move. When at last he raised his head, his breath was coming fast. Drawing a shuddering gulp of air before thrusting her away, he murmured, "I did not mean to do that. It was an impulse."

Her cheeks flamed even brighter and she rubbed her mouth with the back of her hand.

"I beg your pardon," he said curtly, turning away. He walked slowly along the path, whistling for Tarquin, who appeared out of the trees and trotted docilely to his side. Then he turned back to her.

She stood where he had left her, still dragging her hand back and forth across her bruised lips. Her eyes were luminous and staring.

"Why the blazes don't you say something?" He was watching her under half-closed lids.

She thrust her hands behind her back. "As you said, it was an impulse," she replied quietly. "It is not important." She checked him with her hand as he stepped forward. "Truly, I am not a schoolgirl. I have been kissed before. And a kiss is not a calamity." She met his eyes with a small but steady smile. "I know the small value gentlemen such as you place on such trifles. However, I prefer not to be manhandled, however casual the motive."

Drops of rain went unheeded as they stared at each other.

"I must be on my way," Tish said briskly. She bent to gather her hat and shawl from the ground where they had fallen.

Alec shifted his feet uncomfortably. He didn't want to let her go. Not in this mood. Despite her insistence to the contrary, he thought she must be angry with him.

"What errand do you do in Kendal?" he asked, to prolong the conversation.

"Some supplies for the apparatus that fills the balloon." She gave a strong tug to the ribbons under her chin. The projecting brim of her poke bonnet gave a charming frame to her face but also obscured her features when she turned away from him, as she now did.

His wide mouth thinned and he scowled. "I had hoped you were through with that contraption."

She would not look at him. "I did not say we were through," she said firmly, enunciating each word over-carefully. "We will fly the balloon again. As soon as a few problems are resolved." She peeked up at him. "It is no concern of yours, milord," she added severely.

"I am well aware of that, ma'am. Though I should be sorry to see your neck broken."

"Pray do not concern yourself," she insisted loftily. "Good afternoon."

"I . . . wait. Please wait a moment, Lady Letitia. I want to ask you something. George and I go tomorrow to take tea at the White Lion Inn with new friends. They heard George speak of you and asked that you be included in the invitation. Will you join us?"

She plucked at the fringe of her shawl. "I think I had better not," she said meaningfully.

"You make me feel as guilty as a schoolboy," he exploded. "I apologized for kissing you, dammit. It was an impulse. Nothing more. I shan't do it again."

She straightened up and glared at him. "You need not say that again," she snapped. "I care nothing for your kisses." She shrugged. "My affections, however, are engaged and I do not think the gentleman would like me kissing every pedestrian *or* horseback rider on the Kendal road."

"I quite understand. In that case, let us not refer to it further. And since it will never happen again, and you have my word on that, the incident can be forgotten. In any case I mention the subject of tea for a reason that has absolutely nothing to do with you and me. You are concerned about George, I perceive, and he has been down in the dumps these last few days. We were supposed to take tea with these friends a week ago but Lady Lansdale was ill and George has not wanted to go farther from the house than the lake. I have at last persuaded him to go as far as Ambleside. I believe it would cheer him immensely if you would come along."

"Surely your new friends can do that," she retorted.

Taking a deep breath, he smothered an angry reply. "The lady is full of edifying information," he said deliberately, "and her brother is a pleasant but not willing tourist. Both admirable people. But you are needed. You are aware of how much George enjoys your company, my dear girl."

Her wide brown eyes sparkled as she said angrily, "I am not your 'dear girl.' And as far as cheering George is concerned, I can do that another time. When we are alone."

Never before had the Earl of Ardenly been so tempted to beat a female! Nevertheless he forced a smile to his lips. "Gammon. You mean you intend to take to the fishing line again. Now, that's coming too strong."

She thawed unwillingly under the charm of his smile. "Not fishing necessarily," she wavered. She wanted to say yes, but she knew she should not. Her relationship with this intimidatingly forceful man had no future, and yet it was proceeding to intimacy at an alarming pace.

"Please," he coaxed. "For George."

"I will try to come, but there is work to be done at home and I may not finish in time."

He grinned. "Good. And I promise nothing but praise for nature."

He nodded with satisfaction as she ran gracefully down the hill. Why in blazes had it been so important to placate her, he wondered? George had been as gloomy as a gravedigger, but she could have seen him another time, as she suggested.

And why had he promised not to kiss her? It was a harmless flirtation, she was long out of the schoolroom, had had a season in London, and had, she said, been kissed before.

He smiled. She was an imp, bright and amusing to argue with. Refreshingly naïve despite her quick wit. And delicious to kiss. That thought erased the smile. She had been kissed before. And her affections were engaged elsewhere. Or so she said. He patted Tarquin and adjusted the saddle. Just as well that he had made that promise, he admitted. It was a harmless flirtation but one he should not pursue. He had best concentrate on the problem that had brought him to Grasmere.

CHAPTER 6

Nothing had gone according to plan, Tish grumbled to herself. Everything was turned topsy-turvy. In the first place, she had resolved not to go to tea with George and his friends. But he and Alec had come by to pick her up. They had found her in the barn, covered with black grease and struggling with the new section of pipe that she had bought in Kendal. George had insisted that she clean up and come along. "Like a good girl," he said. And the insufferable Earl had stood there, not uttering a word, but his wicked eyes sparkling and challenging her. Until she had said sullenly that she would come, and had stomped off to wash and hastily don her best afternoon gown.

Then, she had resolved that she would not like these new friends. But she had. True, Olivia prattled too much about lectures, everything from literature to geography, but she was infinitely kind in welcoming Tish to join the party and made her feel quite at home within minutes. When Tish discovered that the skirt of her gown was torn, Olivia had discreetly excused them both and up in her room had sewed up the dangling hem as offhandedly as though all guests arrived for tea in need of repair.

Not only was Olivia kind, Tish thought, she was lovely, radiant in an exquisite pale peach gown with a pelisse of darker peach lace. When the English went to Paris in 1814 after Napoleon's first abdication, they found the French ladies abandoning the strictly Empire clinging fashion. Olivia's gown, in the latest style, had puffed sleeves and a double row of flounces at the hem. Her own gown, Tish realized, was distinctly *passé*. It was to Olivia's further credit that she made no reference to either gown. Furthermore her laugh was musical, her voice soft and sweet, her long, white fingers tapering and graceful and her figure full and womanly. A lovely, kind person. Tish was captivated.

Even Hugh Woffington exceeded her expectations. He admitted with a boyish laugh that he had been forced to come to the far north, as he called it, but he was charmingly attentive to his sister and openly affectionate with her. His manners were faultless, his gay spirits infectious. And he was unabashedly admiring of Tish and her pluck in taking to the air in a balloon.

As for George, who had been supposed to need cheering, he was positively boisterous. He kept them all in gales of laughter with anecdotes about the local gentry, anecdotes that were amusing without being malicious. Tish had never seen him in such high spirits.

And as for Lord Ardenly, whom she had resolved to avoid, he was distantly polite but nothing more. He did not keep away from her but neither did he seek her out. Nor was there any trace in his manner of the easy familiarity that had alarmed her. In short, nothing was as she had expected.

George delivered a jocular lecture with the mock seriousness of a bishop as the party strolled down the lawn from the White Lion Inn. "You will observe the town of Bowness yonder. The edifice conspicuous above the neat, humble cottages is our venerable church. For indeed buildings consecrated to the Almighty should loom above those dedicated to man." Tish giggled at his pontification but he raised a warning hand and continued.

"However, do not be deceived by the unassuming appearance of the town. That, ladies and gentlemen, is the capital port town of the lakes and a great market for such indispensables as fish and charcoal. As you see, the harbor is crowded with vessels, including many fishing boats along the commodious pier. And—aha! Our destination, the Windermere ferry."

George hallooed for the boatman, moored on the opposite side. "You will also note," George whispered loudly, "that our jolly ferryman wears blue trousers and jacket. Typical," he said with a wink, "of the Windermere populace."

Windermere is some ten miles long but the main public ferry crosses just south of the largest island in the lake, Belle Isle, and there the lake is less than six hundred yards, so the boatman wasn't long in coming.

The moment Tish took her seat, her spirits lightened. She liked being upon the water, reveling in the response of the boat to the slightest wave. And, besides, the day was faultless, the wind soft and the sun just bright enough for warmth but not scorching. It would be a crime to waste such a day and such a trip. So she resolutely pulled herself out of the sulks.

Alec smiled fondly at George as they settled themselves. "My dear sir," he joked, "if we pay you a penny a passenger as we did our stalwart rower here, will you continue your discourse? What structure is that there, on the island next to the pier?"

"A penny is far too much," George laughed, "if you ask such simpleminded questions. That, dear sir, is a boathouse. Obviously. Not very large or elegant, but a very welcome shelter against sudden storms."

"And the island," Olivia prompted, "how large is it?"

"Whole thing ain't more than a couple of miles round. A female named Curwen bought the island some thirty years ago and had a semblance of a garden put in and gravel walks laid around the circumference. The house is big and ugly, but she's never there so strangers are allowed to land and stroll about. A few sheep are left to keep the grass down, and they and the caretaker are the full-time residents."

A soft thud announced that they had arrived.

"It's pleasant enough passage for a short trip, but I

wouldn't like to bend my legs into that small space for a longer voyage," Hugh grinned as he jumped ashore. "And you, Lord Ardenly, must be even more cramped than I."

"A bit," he allowed. "Here, Miss Woffington, take my hand and allow me to assist you."

"The water looks inviting," that young lady dimpled, "but I shouldn't like to bathe just yet. Thank you."

"I can manage for myself," Tish said, when he turned next to her. She jumped up nimbly. For a moment he caught her eye and she thought she saw a flash of anger, but it passed so quickly she couldn't be sure.

"As you like," he said indifferently and walked away.

"This spoils it!" George muttered.

"What is it?" Tish whispered.

"Just look. There must be half a dozen parties ahead of us." He gestured and she saw that there were, in fact, several groups of visitors admiring the view.

"It doesn't matter," she said quietly. "We can keep to ourselves."

"I don't like crowds," he said more loudly. "It don't amuse me to walk in a parade, like a herd of sheep."

"There's not such a crowd as that. And anyway you can resume your amusing tour and we can ignore the others."

"How can I forget all those—those tourists," he snapped, "when I'm being elbowed and pushed?"

She took his arm anxiously. This wasn't like her old friend. Olivia and her brother were standing a little apart, unsure what to do. Uncomfortable. "Please don't be upset," Tish soothed. "Let's head toward that grove of pines. Perhaps if we sit and talk the others will finish their walks and leave." She leaned closer to smile into his face. "Remember the game we had of naming the clouds? You used to tease me when I repeated Grand-père's scientific observations of the clouds, until it became our game to give them ridiculous names and absurd explanations for their changing ways."

"They won't leave!" George said bitterly, his voice even

louder. "Obviously they are middle-class cits who must exact their penny's worth of time."

Alec interposed himself between his friend and Tish, taking George's arm himself. "You are making your guests uncomfortable. Look at Miss Woffington and her brother. Look at them," he repeated in a low voice. "They are uncomfortable, George. You do not want to make them so, I'm sure of it. We would all prefer to enjoy the island in privacy, but it cannot be. So let us make the best of it. Very well?"

The two men stood, Alec stern, unwavering in his scrutiny. The convulsive twitching of the muscles in George's face left no doubt as to the conflict of his feelings. Finally he dropped his head and stepped back.

"You are correct, of course," he nodded. "Tish, my apologies." He bowed slightly and then walked to Olivia and her brother. "My apologies for my outburst. It is just that I wanted you to enjoy the island as I always have. But I must accept that the Lake District's new popularity will bring changes. Visitors."

"We ourselves are visitors," Hugh said coldly.

"That proves the power of your sister's charm and your warmth. I no longer perceive you as visitors. Rather, you are friends."

There was another long silence as Hugh considered the apology. He was too good-natured not to relent and said finally, with a grudging smile, "I can understand your reluctance to share your solitude."

"I know the solution. Well, at least a partial solution," Olivia said sweetly. "When we return to London we shall tell all our friends that this is a horrid spot. And thus discourage further visits."

Alec smiled at her gratefully. "Capital idea. But what particulars could you cite?"

"Ah, that's a problem," she replied archly, "for all is truly perfect. Perhaps you could invent a fault or two?"

"Anything to oblige a lovely lady who is also tactful and

kind. Now, what do you think, George? Can we invent a calumny?"

Slightly miffed at being excluded from the bandying as well as the compliments, Tish put herself in Alec's path. "Our most famous poet who resides here, Mr. Wordsworth, has often been heard to complain about the whitewashing of the houses. He feels the color makes the houses too conspicuous and obtrusive on nature's own palette."

"And you agree," Alec said mockingly, "since you assume the natural always improves on the artificial."

"I never said that!" Tish replied sharply. What she had intended as an amusing contribution to the raillery was being taken too literally by that odious man!

"You are consistently against the works of man," Alec insisted.

"Hardly," she said, stung. "In fact, I do not agree. The whitewash is practical, for it weatherproofs the walls. And at times practicality must take precedence over aesthetics: But even you must admit the white houses intrude."

"The ratio heavily favors nature, ma'am. There are few houses and many mountains. Or would you and Mr. Wordsworth prefer that men remove themselves altogether so the landscape can revert to nature entirely?"

"Some things of man *are* out of place here," she shot back. "Such as a horse galloping down a mountain road as though it were a racetrack."

"You are both excellent debaters," Olivia interjected, ever the diplomat. "I envy your skill. And what side do you favor, Lord Lansdale?"

"Whitewash has never been a burning issue with me," he laughed, his good humor entirely restored. "But I own I am grateful that you stopped what was taking on the proportions of a quarrel, so I shall discuss whitewash and then skillfully divert the group's attention to another scheme. Let me see, what can we discuss that is less controversial than whitewash?"

"What about balloons?" Alec snapped. He was furious with himself. For some reason he couldn't resist baiting that sharp-tongued female. "Why don't we abandon Lady Letitia's fascinating subject of whitewash and move on to her favorite topic—ballooning?"

"I never said whitewash was fascinating!" Tish cracked back. Then she chuckled. "It is a ridiculous point to debate, I confess." Reluctantly she smiled and then broke into laughter. "Imagine the consternation of the ton at Almack's if I approached Lady Jersey and begged her opinion on the question of whitewash!"

The notion caught Alec's fancy and he chuckled also, adding, "My dear girl, Lady Jersey is indeed the ultimate social arbiter on taste. Without her approval, no one is admitted to that most exclusive of exclusive clubs, Almack's. As you well know."

"Lady Jersey and her cohorts need not have founded such a club had not the gentlemen retreated to so many clubs just for males that we poor females were left sadly out of things," Tish retorted.

"Just so," he agreed. "And now countless females are brokenhearted each season when they do not receive the coveted voucher to enter Almack's."

"That certainly is not a concern of your circle, milord," Tish teased. "You are of the first rank and Lady Jersey smiles on you and yours."

"As she did on you, I'm positive."

"It was my happy lot to enter those hallowed portals," she grinned. "I fear I did not consult her as to whitewash, however."

"Then perhaps you saw fit to inquire about hogg's holes?" he laughed.

Olivia stirred restlessly and a slight crease wrinkled her brow. "I'm not sure I follow. Why would you consult Lady Jersey about—what is it? Hogg's holes?"

"Lord Ardenly appears too serious to descend to non-sense," Tish said demurely, "but that is what *he* is talking."

"His lordship is not always pompous," Alec smiled. "That is what *she* means." He turned to Hugh, who was asking about local hunts.

"I see," Olivia answered, though she did not.

The party had strolled halfway around the island and Tish's hopeful prediction had come true. The other parties had departed, or at least some had gone and the rest were out of sight so that they were finally alone.

With an adroitness that Tish envied, Olivia maneuvered the party so that she had Tish on one arm and her brother on the other. George and Alec fell behind, engrossed in the possibilities involved in fishing from a pier rather than a boat.

"Now we shall really be able to enjoy our stroll," Olivia said cheerfully, "and at the same time Hugh and I shall be able to learn more about your fascinating project, Lady Letitia."

"Please, call me Tish. As George says, we should not stand on formality here."

"Thank you, Tish. And you must call me Olivia. And this scoundrel, here, Hugh."

"Yes, please," her brother seconded. "And I would be fascinated to learn more of your balloons. I am woefully ignorant on the subject and I am quite sure it is one topic that my sister has not heard explored in a lecture. What is the balloon made of? And how on earth do you inflate it?"

Blooming under his genuine enthusiasm, Tish explained. "The balloon itself is a very light silk, and it is made airtight by five coats of a special kind of linseed oil varnish.

"You see, silk is both light and strong but of course it cannot resist the weather and therefore must be varnished. The only drawback," she smiled, "is that the varnish becomes very sticky in hot weather. Such balloons are very liable to catch fire spontaneously, so care must be taken in their storage."

"It sounds as though there is great risk and you haven't even left the ground," Olivia shuddered.

"We take great care," Tish promised her.

"But how do you inflate it?" Hugh asked.

"Hydrogen. We have a furnace and we built a couple of old cannon into it—actually, any cylinders of iron would do. These are heated until they are white-hot and then filled with iron turnings. Water over them makes steam. And the steam over the iron generates hydrogen." She smiled at the expression of total bafflement on Olivia's face. "Understanding chemistry isn't important, Olivia. You may trust in it, hydrogen is released when the steam passes over the iron. We trap the hydrogen in tubes that lead into the balloon."

"That must take forever," Hugh said.

"A few hours. Not so much."

"And is your balloon very large?"

"Sadly, no. It is, as my grandfather says, *petit*. But it is large enough. Perhaps one day soon you will see it."

"I should like that very much," Olivia assured her, "though I've understood very little of what you've said."

"You will be staying on at the White Lion?" asked Tish.

"My sister is daily more enthralled by the District and its people," Hugh grinned. "It seems we shall extend our visit a few more weeks."

A delicate rose flush stole over Olivia's cheeks and she admitted, "I am in no hurry to leave."

"I'm so glad," Tish said fervently. "I wish I had met you when I was in London. I know I would have enjoyed it more."

Pressing Tish's arm gently, Olivia turned her aside so that they separated from Hugh. "Did you find it lonely?" she said softly.

"Yes." There was a tremulous sigh. "And I know it was entirely my own doing. I went down to London unwillingly. You see, before that I had been packed off to a young ladies' academy in Bath, much against my wishes. The girls there were much more sophisticated than I, though younger, and so I kept to myself and had no friends."

She shook her head at Olivia's murmur of sympathy. "No, it was not sad. The studies were nonsense—French, music and such. I speak fluent French and Grand-père taught me to play the piano when I was a child. He also instructed me in science. The French are much more advanced in science than the English, though I've never dared say so before. And he taught me history. But what I did like about the school was that there was an excellent library. I read all the time and so I was content."

"And then you went to London," Olivia said.

"Yes, and unwillingly. I felt I had been away from home forever. My grandfather needs me. But he insisted. Nanny pushed him, as she had about the school. Some cousins agreed to present me because we paid for their own daughter's season. They hadn't a penny. Naturally, the cousins didn't want me. They laughed at me behind my back and said I was tall as a maypole and must marry a giant, if at all. Anyway, I felt horrid with them and assumed that all the girls I met would be as standoffish as the girls at school. So I became standoffish, thinking I would snub them rather than wait to be snubbed.

"I realize now that I closed off any chance at real friendships."

"How honest you are to admit you are the cause of your own loneliness," Olivia exclaimed. "I don't think I could do as much."

"It comes a trifle late," Tish said dryly. "Two years too late."

"But you can visit London again. I know!" Olivia beamed. "You can visit us when the season starts in the fall. Mama comes up for a few weeks at least and would be delighted to have you."

Tish pressed the girl's hand. "You are good, dear Olivia. And I am grateful. But I must remain at home. My grandfa-

ther is ill, you see. And my mother is an invalid. I must stay
home."

"But you mustn't cut yourself off," Olivia protested.

"It's not that I must. I want to."

"I quite understand, but one has to . . ." Olivia faltered.
"One has to make the most of one's opportunities. I am
twenty, Tish, and I know my looks are pleasing and my fortune satisfactory, so I was not anxious my first season to make
a good match. But time slips by fast and one must seize the
chance." She blushed a bright pink at her frankness.

"I know," Tish agreed. "I am twenty-three, which means I
am practically on the shelf. And that was yet another hitch in
London. I was already older than the other girls coming out
for their first season, yet they knew how to flirt and behave
and I did not. In any case, I am resigned to being a spinster.
It is not the worst of fates. Truly. In another year or two I
shall put on a cap," she concluded cheerfully.

Tish was deliberately lighthearted, but the other girl could
not smile in return. It was too bad to think that Tish's
chance had passed her by, and the thought of life as a spinster was horrid to Olivia's mind.

They had circled back to the dock and neither spoke as
they waited for the men to join them. Olivia was preoccupied
with what she foresaw as her friend's dismal future and Tish
was lost in contemplation of lost opportunities, thrown away
by her folly. She raised her eyes to the scenery for comfort.
Laburnums ringed the island and the pendulous yellow blossoms were waving frantically, for the sky had darkened and
the soft breeze had vanished. It was turning blustery. Small
spumes of white water skidded across the lake. The hillsides
in the distance were laced with veins of gold from the brooms
that were now in their full glory.

"Hugh, summon our brawny boatman," George called out
gaily as he approached. "We shall have to devise a means of
keeping our ladies warm while we wait!" And seizing Tish's
hand, George spun her away to waltz down the length of the

pier and back, humming loudly a melody that had captivated London that year.

Following his lead, Alec bowed formally to Olivia and then took her hand. They, too, dipped and turned across the rough, wooden planks. Alec was surprisingly graceful for such a large man and Olivia was a perfect partner, tall enough to match his pace. Tish and George were less well matched, for he was not an inspired dancer for all his eagerness, and she was too tall to fit comfortably in his arms. In fact, they had never danced together before. She didn't think about that, however, but wondered instead about the hectic flush on his face and his abnormal exuberance.

"Look, here comes Charon to ferry us, but not across the Styx, thank heaven. We must leave off dancing," George panted, "but not for long. I think we shall have a proper ball at Lansdale Hall to entertain our new friends." He called to the others and told them of his inspiration. "And tell me, sweet Tish, shall I hum then also or shall we hire musicians?"

"Perhaps one or two fiddlers," she smiled, "so that you might have a chance to drink champagne and waltz."

"And you, Miss Woffington, will you grace my ball?"

Olivia and George fell with delight to discussing the plans. The young lady was describing at length a party she had attended just before leaving London when George laughingly interrupted her.

"Forgive me," he smiled, "but I have just remembered that a ball will not only be a pleasure, but a necessity. We must entertain our new houseguest. Is that not correct, Ali?"

Ardenly shrugged. "I did not know I was famous for my social instincts."

"Not you," George crowed. "Regina."

The only response was a quizzical lift of one black eyebrow.

"Regina," George repeated. "Mama had a note from her this morning. I had forgotten to mention it. It seems that her father has been seized by an urge to renovate and remodel the family manse. The hammering alone is enough to drive her mad, Regina writes, much less the intrusion of workmen into every nook and cranny. And so she has written to ask if she might visit. To escape, you understand." He smiled conspiratorially. "That's what she writes."

"Then that must be the case," Alec said dryly. "Perhaps you might clarify the young lady's identity for your mystified listeners."

"Of course," George turned to the others. "It could not possibly be that the lovely Regina had heard of Ardenly's presence here, eh? I'm sure you know her, Miss Woffington, Lady Regina Douglas."

"We have not been presented," Olivia replied, "but I could not help but notice her, of course, for she is always the most lovely, most elegant lady wherever she goes." Her tone was a trifle wistful. "Who could help but notice her?"

"I certainly noticed her," Hugh agreed enthusiastically, eliciting a sigh from his sister. "I hear she was voted the Incomparable by the bow window crowd at White's. And with a fortune to match, I understand. Whenever we saw her there was a crowd of men six deep around her and all of them the pick of the crop. But, by Jove, it should be another story here."

"Hugh!" Olivia exclaimed.

"You know what I mean, Liv. Beautiful, clever and an heiress to boot."

"I fear he is correct," George chuckled, "she is the Incomparable of the season. In one thing you mistake the matter, Hugh. I fear you'll find competition equally formidable here. Not in numbers, of course. I, for one, do not mean to dangle after the lady. She ain't to my taste. But Ardenly here is another matter. Regina is known as the Incomparable, as you say, and the Earl of Ardenly, Alexander Grenfell, is the Nonpareil. Of all the Regency bucks none shoots straighter, drives better horses, or cuts a finer figure with the ladies. And he most definitely had made progress with this particular lady before we left London. Let us agree that the lure for the lady's visit is not solitude nor scenery."

Another shrug. "Perhaps it would be wisest to allow the lady in question to comment on her own motives," Alec said quietly.

"You are tact itself," George acknowledged with a slight bow. "Tact itself."

The teasing note had left his voice and the sound made Tish shiver. George was different, she thought. What was the matter? Ever since he had come home this time there had been a strangeness in him. Alec, she frowned. Alec made the difference. He was the disturbing element and she heartily wished him gone. The Incomparable and the Nonpareil indeed. Lost in her own disturbing thoughts, Tish was unaware that George, Olivia and her brother had returned to details of the forthcoming ball. In the midst of the happy chatter, Alec drew Tish aside.

"Hugh tells us that you have invited him and his sister to see your balloon someday soon. Does this mean you have repaired your apparatus?" She nodded curtly and turned away.

"Wait!" he commanded imperiously. "I have something to say to you. You should not experiment with the balloon again. It is too dangerous for a woman."

"I remind you *again*, Lord Ardenly, that I am not your responsibility."

"You are not, and I thank God for that, madam. However, since your guardian does not use common sense, some sane advice is in order. I cannot be silent now any more than I could keep still while an army marched into a deadly trap because of an inept general."

"We are not on military maneuvers, Lord Ardenly. Pray allow me to rejoin my friends."

"And nothing I say can dissuade you? Please, I ask you. At least put it off for a while and consider the matter. Don't you realize how dangerous it can be?"

"No," she said curtly and walked off.

Alec's lips tightened and the strange brown-green of his eyes darkened almost to black with the stormy violence of his thoughts. "Then you alone are responsible for the consequences," he muttered, "and I shall put it out of my mind."

CHAPTER 7

The tap at the door was more of a scratch and it was repeated twice before Tish roused herself from her reverie by the fire and ran to answer.

"Pray, miss, I beg your pardon for disturbin' you but I buried my husband and three children all in one grave only yesterday and burying is very dear."

"All four!" the girl exclaimed in horror.

"Yes'm. 'Twas the cholera and it threw the county in such alarm it was thought necessary to burn every article in the house. To prevent the spreading, you see." She fingered her tattered skirt. "I was given clothes by the parish. Wasn't much we had and now it's all gone. And them, too."

The woman's age was impossible to discern, for her face was as wrinkled as a crone's. Yet her hands, outstretched in despair, were those of a young person, despite being chafed and red.

"Please, do come in. Here, sit by the fire and I will fetch you a cup of tea and something to eat."

"Oh, no. I shouldn't like to come in, miss. And please believe me that this is the first time I've begged. But I started walking yesterday and kept going, sleeping in a field, and I'm so weary and down. Just a halfpenny, miss. That would be kindness."

"You shall have your halfpenny. But first you must come in and rest and refresh yourself."

Tish propelled the woman into the hallway with a gentle but firm arm and directed her into the sitting room, but the woman would not take a chair.

"You're the soul of mercy, miss, but I belong in the kitchen—if anywhere."

Tish thought a moment. "I do not agree," she said finally, "but if you would be more comfortable in the kitchen then that is where you shall go."

She served her a generous portion of bread and giblet pie and while the woman was eating, she tied a loaf of black bread and a large slice of the pie in a napkin. Tish knew better than to tax the woman with conversation—she was clearly too tired and desperate for that. But she did press a handful of pennies upon her as she departed and watched with aching heart as the woman trudged out of sight.

"Like as not she left them cholera sicknesses on the chair or plate," grumbled Nanny behind her back. "And you cannot be enriching every soul that calls at the door. You that hasn't had a new gown in the two years since you went to London. I'll wager your dress looked dowdy enough beside that Miss Woffington, who you said was so elegant in her puffed sleeves and flounces. What will you wear to Lord Lansdale's ball, tell me that?"

For an answer, Tish hugged her hard. "Her life will only get worse, Nanny, you know that. She'll probably end up working in one of those dreadful mills. And only think, her husband and three children buried at once! And that taking the last of her money." She shuddered and hugged the old woman again, this time seeking, not giving, comfort.

"Hush!" Nanny raised a finger to her lips. "Is that your mother, now? I'd best go see." She hurried out.

The knocking at the door this time was decisive and unmistakable.

"Nanny," Tish called quietly, peering up into the darkness of the second-floor landing. "There's someone at the door."

"I hear, I hear," hissed the old woman. "But I cannot quiet her so fast. You must turn them away."

"Perhaps if I don't answer?" But there was no word from

above, only those same strange, faint shouts that had sent Nanny running, and the knocking at the door was insistent.

Her steps faltering, Tish pulled open the heavy oak door.

"Good morning, dear Tish," warbled Olivia Woffington. "Lord Ardenly and I are taking a ride—his landau has just arrived from London—and we thought to call and pay our respects to your mother and grandfather."

Speechless, Tish looked from Olivia to Alec to the landau and back. The smart yellow carriage was drawn by a tandem of spirited chestnuts, a groom holding the reins while a bright-eyed boy of about fifteen, also in livery, the groom's assistant or so-called tiger, stood by the head of the lead horse. Olivia and Alec were brimming with vitality and good spirits, though the smile on the Earl's face began to fade as Tish continued to stare.

"My brother and Lord Lansdale have forsaken us to bathe in the lake." Even Olivia's admirable aplomb faltered under Tish's stricken silence. "We plan a sail later and—and hope you might accompany us."

"I cannot," Tish blurted out. "Thank you for thinking of me." Still she made no move to invite them in.

"As Miss Woffington explained," Alec added impatiently, "we came to pay our respects to your mother and grandfather." Stepping forward, he almost got one elegantly booted foot over the doorsill. "May we come in?"

With a quick sidestep, Tish edged past him, pulling the door closed behind her.

"Forgive me for not being more hospitable," she said slowly. "My wits are slightly addled this morning. You see," she paused, her attention riveted on Alec's cravat, "you see, we had a domestic catastrophe this morning." She flashed a relieved smile. "This is a very old house and the roof fell in. The ceiling fell, rather. The one in the parlor. Well," she continued happily, "naturally the whole house is full of grit and dust and I cannot possibly invite you in. I am desolate."

"Was anyone harmed?" Olivia asked anxiously.

"Oh, no. The furniture is a trifle damaged but nothing of importance," Tish declared loftily.

"How fortunate. I recall an instance similar to this in the old dower house on my parents' estate. It was during a party my grandmother was giving. The butler was in the pantry fetching serving plates when half the shelves fell down upon him. He was cascaded with Sèvres china, knocked unconscious and badly cut."

While Olivia detailed a description of the debacle and the ensuing difficulty in assembling proper china for the dinner, Alec muttered under his breath in Tish's ear, "And how miraculous that you yourself have escaped the shower of dust and grit." He tweaked a lock of her shining hair and smiled grimly as she jerked away.

"In any case, dear Olivia," Tish said, emphasizing that woman's name and ignoring her companion, "in any case, Grand-père does not receive company. His arthritis does not permit it. You are considerate to think of it and I will convey your respects. He will be pleased, I know." She was obviously dismissing her callers.

"Is it possible that you have forgotten your dear mother?" Alec asked sarcastically.

"Impossible," Tish flushed. "She is bedridden and cannot have company."

"I thought that if we met you might be allowed to make us a short visit in London this fall," Olivia explained. "But I will leave a note on my calling card." She took a tiny white square from the dainty green reticule hanging from her arm. Today Olivia was all spring green, from her thin cotton frock to the enormous bow that showed three curls tumbling in artful disarray from under her bonnet.

"You look lovely," Tish smiled sincerely. "As fresh and soft as the morning."

Since Tish was again in her country clothes, the dark-gray skirt, blue-checked apron, and wooden-soled clogs, even tactful Olivia was hard put to return the compliment. But she was seldom at a loss and this was no exception.

"And you, dear Tish, are charmingly clad for helping clear away the debris. Isn't it typical of Tish that she would lend a hand to the housekeeper, Lord Ardenly?"

"Typical," he agreed seriously. "I am convinced that Lady Letitia is consideration itself to her indoor staff. Just as she is reputed to be with those who work out of doors."

Tish stiffened at the unmistakably droll accent, but his face retained its habitual mask of lazy indifference.

"Thank you. I wish I could say the same of you, Lord Ardenly, but I refrain from snap judgments."

"I sent off yesterday for a new gown from London," Olivia chimed in, oblivious to the barbed insults being exchanged before her. "Lord Lansdale's ball is only a fortnight away and as he is to have a large house party, there will be other festivities as well. Will you get your gown from London, or have you a local genius with the needle?"

Flushing, Tish looked down. "I had forgotten about it."

"But you are coming. You must!" Olivia cried.

"If you have finished cleaning the debris?" offered Alec.

Olivia looked from one to the other in bewilderment. "How could it take a fortnight to clean the debris? And how should that interfere?"

"Pay him no mind," Tish snapped. "Of course I shall come."

"Do you like to dance?" Alec asked suddenly.

That man delighted in keeping her off balance, Tish scowled. Changing moods like a chameleon, one moment teasing, the next sounding like an old friend. She looked up uncertainly but found no irony in his eyes. "Yes, I love to dance."

They both smiled.

"I have some of the newest fashion magazines at the inn," Olivia volunteered. "Come take tea with me tomorrow and we can dissect the latest styles."

Tish gave her a quick kiss on the cheek. "I'd like that very much. Thank you, Olivia. Thank you for coming."

She waved farewell until the landau had gone around the bend in the lane. Then it was with reluctance and dragging steps that she entered the house, and if she could have known about a conversation the visit would prompt, she would have been even more unsettled. Far more than a conversation, it was an interrogation. Alec had come away from his visit to Tish with a dozen questions in his mind and he insisted that George must have the answers.

For one thing, he told George, it was obvious that Tish was lying. Obvious to him, that is, though not to kind Olivia. The intertwining tumble of honeysuckle and roses over the parlor windows mostly obscured the interior, but what he could see made it clear that the parlor was intact. The ceiling had not fallen. Not that he needed that graphic proof to know he was being told a tale. The girl had stepped out of the house at their knock and there wasn't a speck of dirt on her. She was, in fact, "shining" clean. Finally, there would have been at least a servant carrying beams or chairs or something out of the place if such a thing had occurred. Why would she lie?

Even more disturbing to him was the contradiction between what George had told him of Tish's circumstances and what he could see with his own eyes. When George protested that he did not understand, he did not perceive a contradiction, Alec snorted that the man was blind. The discussion digressed as they argued heatedly about George's sensibilities. But eventually both men cooled and Alec outlined his case.

First, Tish's father reputedly was a man of means in the pay of the government. Salaries were not astronomical but they were substantial. Where was evidence of his inherited money or his salary? The grounds around the house were sadly neglected, showing an absence of gardeners. The house itself was ramshackle, in need of that damnable whitewash. The door was opened by Tish herself, not a butler. And obviously the girl had no fashion magazines and no new ball gowns. If not, why not? The young ladies of Alec's acquaintance had closets full of new gowns. Olivia fit his conception and his experience of females. Tish did not. A lack of money explained all of the above. But if there was a lack of money, why was it so?

George could not answer. He conceded that what Alec said was true—and always had been, so long as he could remember. The grounds had always been unkempt, the garden consisting of what Tish planted and cared for; the paint outside always peeled; the servants were always invisible. He had given it no thought, he excused himself, because his encounters with Tish were always away from the house, out on the fells and lakes. He simply had never been invited inside. He had never seen her mother. Her grandfather he had glimpsed from afar but he had never exchanged a word with him. He accepted it without question.

But how could he not question? Alec persisted. There was a mystery to that household—a secret about that girl.

Nothing strange about Tish, George retorted. She had come to Lansdale Hall to dine occasionally. And surprisingly enough she and Lady Lansdale hit it off well, as both shared an avid interest in history and politics. Both were individualists. As for the father, the government directed men to make sacrifices and perhaps staying in foreign posts was his. Anyway, wearing old clothes and disdaining fashions was part of Tish; he would thank Alec to stop criticizing his friend.

The two men talked through two bottles of the marquess' finest cognac until the tapers burnt themselves out, and they were no more in accord at the end than when they began. George was content and Alec was not. Not at all.

CHAPTER 8

The stable hand doffed his cap and a gaggle of stableboys scattered like flies as the Earl of Ardenly strode in, trailed by his groom Stramm and his tiger.

"I saw it first," the latter panted, struggling to keep up with the Earl's long strides. "It was me that first noticed. Call his lordship, I tells Stramm. His lordship will want to check on this hisself."

Alec cut short the boy's tirade with a quelling glance. "Well, Stramm?"

"He was a bit off his feed yesterday," the man admitted grudgingly. "I thought it were on account of the storm. Never knew a horse what cared for thunder. And you can be sure I didn't leave Tarquin one minute. Gave him an extra currying to calm him, I did."

Moving his hands lightly over Tarquin's massive body, studying his eyes, attentive to the whinny of his greeting, the Earl frowned. "And today?"

"Wouldn't touch his food, that's what," the sharp-eyed tiger interjected.

"Not so." The groom glared at the boy. "Just didn't eat it all. And didn't seem himself, not so feisty, if you catch my meaning."

"And his eyes ain't bright like usual," the tiger continued. "Always study the eyes, I say." The words died in his throat as he caught the full force of the Earl's imperious regard.

"You are an insolent pup, though correct in your assumptions. Now keep still. Your task is to assist Stramm. That is all." He didn't raise his voice but the threat behind his measured tone registered even with the excited lad. He took a quick step to one side, put his hands respectfully behind his back and nodded.

"Now, Stramm, may I hear your remedy for Tarquin's malaise?"

Stramm was torn between a desire to cuff the insolent tiger and the awe in which he held his master. Clenching his fists, he managed to answer that he felt the cause of Tarquin's indisposition must be the change in his feed. He couldn't resist adding that with his fifteen-plus years as his lordship's head groom, and serving his father before him, he did not need any stripling to tell him his business.

The Earl listened to this rambling report without noticeable impatience, but a glint in his eye warned Stramm that he had best be concise and leave his feud with the tiger for later.

"And how is the fodder here different from that in London or Somerset or Spain?"

"I'm sure I can't say, your lordship. It is damper here but within the stables it's warm and dry. And there's no sickness among the other horses we brought or the estate's cattle."

"Food nothing," the irrepressible tiger hooted. " 'Tain't nothing different about the hay. He's bewitched, that's what. Bewitched."

"I am not known for my patience," his master said without taking his eyes from Tarquin, "and I tell you, boy, if you start playing the fool with me, you'll regret it."

"But it's true. I've seen it with my own eyes. There's a hag that comes creeping in the back way each dawn. She slips into the big house by a side door, an open door, mind you, and the rest of them doors bolted like Old Bailey. She's a witch, I reckon, casting spells."

"That's enough!" The heavy black brows were a thunderous slash across the furrowed brow. Alec grabbed the boy by the collar of his jacket and held him dangling two feet off the ground. "I'll have no more nonsense about witches or spells. And no more spying about the house." He shook the boy as though he were a naughty pup.

"If I recall, you were a chimney sweep when I found you literally asleep in the gutter. A failed chimney sweep, that is, who had been dismissed for helping yourself to trinkets on your way out the door. If your master hadn't kept the things himself, you'd have been in prison. Are you eager to return to the gutter, boy?"

He dropped him so abruptly, the lad fell into a heap at his feet.

"Well?" he growled.

"No, sir. I mean, yes, sir. I won't talk no more about it." He scrambled to his feet, his eyes bright with unshed tears and swallowed hard. "You won't turn me off? I've been so happy here."

"What concerns you is the horses," Alec said sternly. "Mind your business and you shall stay." He waved him aside. "Stramm, fodder will be brought from the Somerset estate. I cannot think a change in food could cause Tarquin to sicken, he has never been so cosseted. But there may be something hereabouts that disagrees with him. In the meantime, keep him warm and away from other horses and other people. You may make your bed with him here so that all visitors are discouraged."

His frown eased somewhat as he noted his groom's gloomy visage. "This stable is as elaborate a construction as the house itself, my friend—indeed, as Buckingham Palace. I dare say you will contrive to be comfortable."

"Yes, m'lord, whatever you say," the groom replied with a sigh.

There was a timid pluck at the Earl's sleeve. "You promise I can stay?" the tiger ventured timidly.

"Your future is a matter of indifference to me," Alec shrugged, "but I do not like to see any living creature descend those infernal chimneys. Do your job and you shall have a place. And do not pinch any trinkets." He gave Tarquin a gentle caress.

There was a twinkle in his eyes as he retraced his steps. Had it been any other horse he would have overlooked such minor symptoms. In fact, the truth was probably that Tarquin was not being given the exercise he needed. The fodder from Somerset wouldn't help. But it did no harm to keep his staff alert.

"Impossible, sir," Ruddick protested. "Impossible to transport fodder here from Somerset in forty-eight hours. How can it be done?"

"I do not know," Alec said calmly. "Please see to it. I'm sure you will manage somehow." He studiously ignored the disapproval sparkling from behind Ruddick's wire-frame spectacles.

"By the by, have you seen the boy's hag?" He didn't look up from the mail on the desk before him.

"If you will excuse the observation, it was your own instructions that I look into the goings-on of the household. Very little escapes my reconnaissance. I most certainly have seen the woman in question."

"Quite so," Alec smiled. "You perform admirably, always. You have only yourself to blame, my dear fellow, if I have come to expect herculean accomplishments from you."

Slightly mollified, Ruddick explained that he had inquired as to the hag's identity, and learned that she visited the Dowager Marchioness in her bedroom every morning. Lady Lansdale always sent her maid out of the room while the visitor was with her. Her name was Maude and she was known for being a country healer dealing in herbs and such.

One of his letters must have been especially engrossing, for the Earl only nodded to dismiss Ruddick. But he had, in fact, taken Ruddick's words to heart though he was not greatly surprised. He had suspected that the Marchioness' behavior was influenced by drugs. A more worrisome thought was how this affected George.

Ruddick, for his part, was distracted by his impossible assignment. His lordship was a trifle spoiled, he mused. No more than all the gentry, of course. Used to giving orders, he was, and always a regiment of footmen and maids and grooms to do his bidding. And why not? They were well recompensed for their labors, would always be assured of a roof over their heads, and the work was seldom onerous. When his lordship traveled, as now, the staffs at the London house and country estate had themselves a fine rest. And his lordship was scrupulously fair. And a brave soldier.

Inspiration struck and Ruddick relaxed. He would dispatch a groom with the message to the Somerset estate manager. Let the swiftness of the mission be on *his* head, not Ruddick's. That settled, the valet should have been happy but he was not.

Ruddick was unhappy in the Lake District. He disliked the country in general, and this dislike had deepened since the Dowager Marchioness had begun preparations for the house party and ball. The whole place was being turned upside down, and a man never knew where he could step without having some female screech that he was tracking on her newly waxed floors or sitting on her freshly scrubbed settee. Ruddick longed for the peace of his lordship's bachelor establishment.

What he saw was only the tip of the iceberg. In the house itself the stout, key-rattling housekeeper was a scourge to the ranks of servants below her. The curtains were never whisked quite to her matronly satisfaction the first time. The softest linen was dipped in fresh milk and water to sponge the floor carpets again and again. And the venetian blinds were turned first this way and then that so the duster might reach every single inch of them, and this, too, over and over.

In the high-vaulted cavern that was the kitchen, a dozen

extra girls from the country were at work assisting the regular staff as kitchen, vegetable and scullery maids. "Frenchy," her ladyship's chef, was inspired to create the fanciest, most delectable treats of his culinary career. Provisions must be imported—loins of beef, venison, geese, turkeys, salmon, turbot, mutton, tongue, sausages—and readied for the fire. Heaping platters of vegetables, egg-rich pigeon pies, hams, currant tarts, gooseberries, melons and fruits of all kinds, mulligatawny and turtle soups, all these would emerge in due course. The chef chuckled with satisfaction as he pored over recipes and wrote out menus in a fine Gallic script for her ladyship's approval.

Downstairs, in the wine celler, the steward browsed through the dusty stacks, refreshing his memory as to the location of each and every vintage. Whatever "Frenchy" proposed, he was ready.

Despite all this, it was out of doors that the most elaborate preparations were under way. Lady Lansdale had sent for an architect who was the current darling of London society. Her order caused him first to gasp and then to chortle with glee. She told him to design and construct a dozen different follies about the estate. He had, she added casually, three weeks. Each folly was to be outstanding—beautiful, surprising, or exotic.

After all, she reminded him, a folly is a whimsical or extravagant structure, a conversation piece or a structure to lend interest to a view or commemorate an event.

Workmen were summoned from the Dorset estate and the labor commenced. With boundless energy the architect darted from place to place, unrolling scrolls of plans, pointing, measuring and giving orders.

First something for the sentimental. On the crest of a grassy hill he placed a Gothic ruin, a tall, slender arch on a base just large enough for two chairs and a table. Ivy creepers curtained the place. Gracing another promontory was a sturdier Athenian arch, this topped with statuary and urns, and inscribed on the columns in Latin verse were tributes to Wellington.

For spice, the architect situated a miniature Chinese pagoda against a tangle of briar hedges; entry was only by a willow-patterned bridge set over a stream. A miniature Spanish castle had an equally diminutive moat. For whimsy, two mechanical doves sang on golden perches in a giant wicker cage. A duplicate birdcage had empty swings and an open door. A shepherd's cottage with a perpetually burning fire in the grate boasted a flock of immaculate lambs in its wee garden. Walking a plank into a tiny ship, one found a half-opened chest with fake jewels and a bloody flag with skull and crossbones.

A compact Norman castle was judged too serious, and the round table was replaced with gaming tables for hazard and faro. Expert application of a few boulders created an instant pond to the rear of the house, and the bridge over it was so narrow that only one person could pass at a time, except where it widened slightly in the center. And when one stepped on those middle planks, a concealed device set off musical chimes. A gazebo in the thickest part of the woods was filled with herbs of the strongest, most pungent scents.

Unquestionably the most fantastic folly was on the great lawn fronting the mansion. The lawn itself was circular, and in the center were eight tall columns of rose-colored stone. Atop those columns, accessible only by a swaying rope ladder, was a tent of pink silk furnished with heaps of thick pillows.

The extravagance of the dozen follies made even the Earl pause, and his own fortune was considerably larger than that of his good friend George or his mother. Lady Margaret had continued to behave erratically, shifting without warning from near hysteria to apathy to more normal behavior. Was she, Alec worried, exhibiting yet another sign of instability with her grandiose schemes? He puzzled over the problem without knowing how to broach the question to either mother or son. Happily, the lady herself volunteered the answer.

It happened late one afternoon when the Earl was returning from a solitary ride. Several days had passed since Tarquin's first signs of indisposition and he was now obviously in perfect health. Feed from Somerset had not arrived within forty-eight hours, but it was not long thereafter in coming. It was the regular exercise, in any case, which Alec felt had worked the cure. Whatever the cause, normalcy prevailed in the stables once again.

The Dowager Marchioness intercepted Alec as he approached the house. "I am going to visit the shepherd's cottage, Lord Ardenly. Would you care to accompany me? I understand it is all but finished."

"Of course, Lady Margaret. Is this the last folly to be completed?" Alec held out his arm. The path was still slippery underfoot from a drizzle that morning. The hand she put on his arm was light as a bird's touch.

"The Spanish castle still needs work." Her voice today was clear. She was, as always, in black, as incongruous as a black butterfly against the brightly variegated summer flowers.

"Your architect is a versatile and thorough fellow," Alec ventured. "I understand he has sent to London for some furniture and decorations."

"Yes. He has quite ravaged the town house and estate. It is vital that every detail be correct."

"It seems a shame, then," Alec said, "that the follies will be torn down directly the party is over. So much time and care in their construction . . . so much expense, and all for only a few days' pleasure."

Despite his deliberate nonchalance, the nature of Alec's interest was apparently obvious for Lady Margaret ignored his statement and answered his implied question.

"You know, I suppose, that most of society assumes I am dead or dying. I could expect nothing else when I have kept cloistered here so many years. And to me it is a matter of indifference what people think. It was only after you and George came that it occurred to me that I was doing my son an injustice. I have chosen this life, but I would not choose for him."

She halted abruptly as they rounded a grove of oaks and the cottage came into view. She sighed. "Yes, it is quite right." Her head bent, the black lace veil muffling her words, she continued to speak and Alec was forced almost to crouch to hear her words.

"Ostentation and originality are what I asked the architect to give me. Only a small part of society will be at this party, but all of the *haut ton* will hear of it. Our guests will be envied by those who are not present, they will be entertained by the follies, and the whole event will be remarked. My place and especially that of my son will be secured once again. It is the least a mother can do, do you not agree, Lord Ardenly?" The bone of her fleshless fingers pressed hard into his arm.

Taken aback by her reasoned statement, Alec was at a loss for words. "I—I applaud your action, Lady Margaret." He felt he owed her the truth. "The thing is that George already moves in the best society in London. I think perhaps you exaggerate the situation a bit. He has not suffered nor, indeed, has your own reputation. On the other hand, your party will certainly set society abuzz, which can do no harm."

He frowned. Her face was shadowed and he had no way of knowing whether she was offended or relieved. There was a long silence.

"I'm pleased by your plain speaking. I had perceived there was some worry on his mind. Some concern which caused an unnatural moodiness. My suspicion may be mistaken."

"No one forgets the sights of battle overnight, milady. George is too intelligent to be insensitive."

She murmured something inconsequential and they walked

on. Then she said dispassionately, "I am not a well woman. I must submit to frequent cupping, you know, and application of leeches. My nerves are delicate in the extreme. Yet you shall discover that none of this will afflict the party. I can keep my pain to myself. You shall see, all shall be sacrificed for George."

The crease in Alec's brow deepened and, as before, he failed to find the proper response. "Damn," he thought angrily, "I am once again reduced to the awkward speechlessness of a green boy." Quite involuntarily there sprang into his mind the sparkling brown eyes and spirited independence of the other woman who not long before also had rendered him helplessly inarticulate. Fortunately he had resolved to put *her* out of his mind.

"Look there!" The hiss broke into his reverie.

"There is a sheared lamb in the garden. And it is too soon."

"I understood the clipping season had begun." He was baffled.

She pecked at his sleeve with her sharp nails, a disquieting staccato. "Of course it has, but I want our guests to see the clipping for themselves. This is one of the most important festivals in the Lake country and we shall do what the farmers do after a clipping—we shall have a dance. The clippers expect it and it will be a novelty for our guests. They'll see the clipping and then we'll have the party—ale, bread, cheese, even tobacco for the clippers, just as Squire Daniel does. And a fiddler to play for dancing in the barn.

"How," she concluded, "can we do that if all the lambs are sheared?"

"There must be others," Ardenly suggested. He looked around. "Shall I seek out the gardener or one of the workmen?"

She indicated that that was what she expected him to do and quickly, so Alec set off at a brisk pace to find help. His thoughts were chaotic and a bemused whistle was on his lips. That Lady Margaret should accuse George of moodiness! She of all people.

They started dragging to locate the fox's scent before dawn, so the first rays of light to reach over the hills found the hounds already on the chase and the visitors from London stumbling and falling in their effort to keep pace.

George had explained the procedure as they sat over brandy the evening before. That is, a fox hunt in the District had to be on foot for a horse could easily break a leg in the rocky, uneven terrain of narrow valleys, hidden streams and precipitous crags. Not a few of the dozen gentlemen in the gray pink of the early dawn wondered, however, whether it would not be a man's leg or ankle that would snap instead. Breath was too precious to waste voicing such a pessimistic thought, for the fox and hounds raced like the wind. More importantly, an English gentleman never admits fear or apprehension, however warranted.

Eleven hours later, George, Alec and Hugh, separated from the others, were only too glad to throw themselves on the softest ground available. After a few minutes spent regaining his breath, George looked askance at the indigo bulging clouds that were trundling in over Solway Firth from Ireland.

"We're in for fog. I hope the rest remember what I told them should this happen."

"Surely not fog," Hugh objected. "The sunset is clear."

"Mountains make their own weather, as a dalesman knows. But if the men stay put, they'll be safe. Danger is in trying to move in the fog."

"As I recall," Alec smiled ruefully, "fog blots out and magnifies at the same time, so that staring at an unknown lake at a distance can seem like viewing a puddle five yards away."

"Frankly, I for one should welcome being fogbound," Hugh chuckled. "I don't mind admitting that I am winded, my legs ache and my feet are swollen. And just look at my tatters!" He sat up to display a coat that hung in rags, nailed boots scratched beyond repair, and trousers stained and torn. "And don't grin at me—you fellows are no better. You warned us, George, but I had no idea what it would be."

"Aye, we're a sorry-looking lot," Alec smiled at the others. "But if one is going to scramble over razor-sharp boulders and through thickets of thorns sharp as needles and do all this afoot, one must expect a penalty. I'm glad Tarquin was not doing the same. And for all that, I enjoyed the day enormously. It is, as you predicted, George, more of a challenge than my sort of fox hunting."

George yawned and leaned back on one elbow. "Um . . . the odds are four to one in favor of the fox. I may have forgotten that detail. And those wily creatures must today have scaled up peaks and pelted down hills some thirty miles with us tagging behind."

"What had we bagged when we separated from the rest?" Alec yawned also.

"Be assured, a full share of the motley vermin. Between us all we had at least ten foxes, four badgers, eight or nine wildcats and I don't know how many martens."

"The local sheep will be grateful for that," Hugh grimaced as he flexed his tired back. "Hard enough to catch one fox. Damned clever. I saw a fox disappear along the top of a dry stone wall using his brush for balance. I swear it."

"I believe you," said Alec, smiling at the younger man. "That's why they make such worthy opponents, Hugh. They're crafty and spirited."

"And twice the size of foxes in the shires," Hugh shuddered.

"Most entertaining part of the day was when we lowered Alec on a rope to dislodge that elusive critter who took refuge out of reach on that crag," George chortled. "The look on your face as you went down!" He rolled over, shaking with convulsive laughter.

"I did think we might have tried a bit longer to dislodge him with stones," Alec complained mildly. "And remember I did not volunteer, I was most definitely conscripted." He shifted uncomfortably. Blazes! He'd thrown himself down on lush green that turned out to be damp mosses. He hadn't noticed until the dampness penetrated the fabric of his trousers. He stood cautiously, waiting for muscles to protest the double damage of extreme exertion and the wet. Good, no aches. "If you gentlemen are couched on moss, as I was, I suggest you arise."

Regarding his boots he added, "Ruddick will most certainly think me a liar when I tell him that still another pair of boots are destroyed and these from the claws of a fox."

George had scrambled to his feet, still laughing. "Better your boots than your face, my friend, or other susceptible portions of your anatomy."

"I felt more like the bait than the hunter, true, dangling like a worm at the end of the line."

George snorted. "Perhaps next week we'll give you a try at eagle baiting," he grinned.

"Shall we look for the others or head for home?" Hugh, bending over, was rubbing the calves of his legs. He would feel every step of those thirty miles tomorrow, he thought unhappily.

Alec waited for George to decide. Looking about, he fastened his gaze on Helvellyn, the highest of the mountains, glinting reddish blue in the sunset like a distant beacon. He drew a deep breath. He felt a comfortable fatigue, weariness come of hard, physical effort for a practical reason. Different from the tiredness experienced after a long night at the dice, gambling and drinking.

"Sometimes I miss the war," he said impulsively. "We had the best damned trained infantry in Europe, didn't we? And the best musketry fire."

"Wellington's?" Hugh ventured.

Both George and Alec answered "Of course," then fell silent as if by mutual consent.

"I thought I was lucky to avoid it," Hugh confessed.

"You were," George said slowly, "and yet you were not. The danger was exhilarating and the sense of duty something special, different for each man. I miss it too, sometimes. But the nightmares . . . those I could do without." Facing Alec he nodded, "Time helps. You said it would. Time and friends."

"And this place," Alec agreed, throwing an arm around his friend's neck. "I need a drink and a bath, in that order. And I prescribe the same for you two rapscallions. If we hurry we will miss the fog. See, there it comes."

To the astonishment of his friends, Alec then led them down the hill to the sound of his full, deep voice singing the buffo aria from *Don Giovanni:* "With blondes he praises their kindness, with dark ones their constancy, with the fair ones their sweetness. In winter he prefers them fat, in summer he likes them lean."

By the time they reached Lansdale Hall, the three were singing lustily, even though a trifle off-key.

CHAPTER 9

Tish flopped down in the shade of the stone wall that marked an irregular line behind her home and sighed heavily. The excessive heat of the morning almost made her ill with the headache. Almost, but not quite, for even sunk in gloom as she was, Tish would not allow herself the missish pleasure of succumbing to the vapors. Linen spread for bleaching on the grass ruffled slightly at a stray wisp of warm air, but the leaves of the sycamore overhead hung stone still. There really was no breeze. Tish scowled at the sheets for they reminded her of the balloon and her frustrated dreams.

After tea she would row to Loughrigg Fell, the girl thought. It would be cooler then. And she could gather wild strawberries. The prospect failed to cheer her. Grand-père was correct, of course, that Bowen could not spare the time to tinker with the apparatus or the balloon. The sheep could not wait and she could. But she didn't want to wait—she was restless.

She frowned at the vivid green hills beyond the lake. The frequent deluges of July and August prompted a dark emerald growth everywhere except where the fields were given to hay. The erratic weather, one day scorching hot and the next too cool to bathe in the lake, had always amused her. But not today. It seemed that lately nothing amused her.

Small ferns and geraniums blanketing the stone wall sent out a sharp perfume. Like another distinctive scent, she thought, and grimaced. Her scowl now had nothing to do with the blinding brightness of the sun. It was, rather, the recollection of yesterday's debacle.

Tish had gone to visit Olivia. Over her arm, protected against dust by layers of tissue, she carried the gown she meant to wear at the ball. It had been her mother's and the style was plainly old-fashioned with its full skirt and long sleeves. Tish hoped that Olivia, so clever about such things, might suggest a simple alteration or two that would transform the gown into the latest style, because whether it was stylish or not, the garment would simply have to do. All five gowns that Tish had purchased for her season had emerged from the attic with more holes than a fishing net. Nanny theorized that Tish had not packed them away with care—she had jumbled them into an old trunk without even sponging them clean first. Her mother's gown, to the contrary, had been folded in a bed of mothballs, cushioned in tissue. Forty years old, it was as perfectly preserved as though it had been worn the night before. A lesson, Nanny preached, on taking proper care of things. Tish, who had been in a highly disturbed state when she left London, and who had vowed never to wear a ball gown again, admitted that Nanny was correct. The result of her temper was that she must needs appear dowdy, unless Olivia could save the day.

Tish walked to the White Lion Inn with a quick step. Olivia was a good friend, generous and kind, and surely she would put the dress to rights. The unforeseen complication was Lady Regina Douglas, who was ensconced in the drawing room like a privileged confidante and old chum. She made Tish feel decidedly *de trop*. That exquisite, tiny nymph with her golden curls and large blue eyes, her figure delicate as a violet, her laugh trilling and her smile devastatingly gay, that young lady had wrinkled her pert, tiny nose even while Tish greeted Olivia. And while Tish was being introduced, there was a noticeable moue of distaste on her face.

"How delightful that we three have a chance for a long, cozy talk," Olivia beamed, propelling Tish forward into the room. "Tish is an old friend of Lord Lansdale, Lady Douglas, and knows the Lake District extremely well. Her familiarity with local customs and flora will be invaluable to his lordship's houseguests."

Lady Douglas flashed a dimple. "Yes, I recall George mentioning something about a young person who is knowledgeable about the country. For some reason I had the impression it was a young man, but perhaps there is someone else. In any case, it does seem the party will be great fun, quite . . . rustic and original." Taking a gauzy lace fan from her reticule, she began fanning herself.

Tish stared dumbly at the turkish carpet while Olivia, after a pointed silence, stepped into the breach. "May I pour you a cup of tea, dear Tish? And tell me, Lady Douglas, who else will be in the party?"

She proffered the teacup with no success as Tish mulishly shook her head "no."

"You must call me Regina, please, and I shall call you Olivia. That's why I called upon you today, so that we might become acquainted." Her smile was gay. "It seems there is a handful of neighbors invited, the Squire and his wife among them. And has the Squire children?" she turned to Tish.

"Four daughters and three sons," Tish replied stiffly, noting the slight pout once again whenever Regina faced her way. "I'm not sure which is at home, though. Two of the boys were in the navy and the eldest has been traveling. None of the girls is married."

"Seven children! A hearty squire, indeed. Breeding must be favorable hereabouts."

Tish, wide-eyed, felt a blush suffuse her face and even Olivia, more sophisticated, was taken aback.

Obviously unaware of the effect of her frank remark, Regina went on. "And Lord Lansdale has considerately asked some special friends of Alec's and mine—Lord Ardenly, that is. We have a special circle in London, of course, and are constantly in one another's pockets." She cocked her head. "But what *is* that smell?"

"Smell?" Olivia echoed, fussing with the teapot.

"It's there, there." Lady Douglas moved so quickly that Tish did no more than raise a hand and certainly couldn't stop her. Like a flash, Regina had ripped aside the white tissue and stood, giggling and fanning herself rapidly, holding the gown at arm's length.

"That's it. Apparently that . . . that thing has just now been resurrected from who knows where. Mothballs."

Tish snatched up the garment. "I hadn't time to air it."

"But whatever," the golden curls sparkled, "are you planning to do with it?"

"Wear it to the ball."

Backing away, Regina said judiciously, "Light blue is a sweet color. I often wear it. And it is quite a distinct style. I vow you will certainly be unique." She bumped against the tea tray with a gasp. "Perhaps we could take a turn on the lawn, Olivia. I feel just a trifle faint from the odor.

"And pray don't worry yourself," she reassured Tish sweetly. "My mama says that my sensibilities are too greatly developed and I own it is the truth. I am forced to choose fragrances with care and even so I sometimes have to toss out an entire bottle of the most expensive French perfume. So you have nothing to apologize for."

Since she had never intended to apologize, and in fact that was the furthest thing from her mind, Tish was left totally speechless. She remained rooted while Regina and Olivia gathered parasols and started toward the door. It was only when Olivia gave a gentle tug to her sleeve that she shook her head and came to life again. And for the remainder of Lady Douglas's visit she restricted herself to nods and perfunctory smiles.

Her temper did not improve after Lady Douglas left. Olivia had taken her scissors to several rows of ruffles, had stitched here and there, and finally the gown was a version of the Grecian style with long sleeves. An oddity.

Regarding her image in the pier glass, Tish felt a pang to see that even the pale blue of the silk was unbecoming, to say nothing of the style. "I am ridiculous in this," she groaned. "It would do very well for a candy-puff creature—" she paused significantly, "but *I* am ridiculous in it. The dress is dowdy, the color dreadful, and my long straight hair absurdly juvenile when I am far past the first flush of youth. And it's so—so brown. I look a freak."

"You do not," Olivia said stoutly. "Admittedly you need to curl your hair. And the pale blue is not your best shade. But with your hair curled and pinned up, you will be lovely. With a flower or a ribbon."

"My hair doesn't curl," Tish said flatly. "Not at all. At my aunt's insistence when I was in London I spent entire nights with my hair in rags, barely able to sleep for the discomfort. And two seconds after they were taken out, the hair fell— straight. It's no use. None."

The sympathetic distress of her companion was so immediate and profound that Tish could have bitten her tongue for her thoughtless words.

The gentle creature sighed. "But, Tish, if your hair's pinned up . . . And perhaps a sash or shawl of a stronger color."

An enormous lump in Tish's throat made speech difficult, but she would not encourage the pity she saw in Olivia's eyes.

"Perhaps you are right," she said weakly. "I—I can pin my hair up." She forced a smile. "And then, as you say, a flower or two." She tugged at the neckline of the gown. It was almost indecently low by her standards. "I will add a sash." Encouraged by Olivia's patent relief, Tish made herself grin broadly. "Indeed, that's just the thing. I shall add a sash in a bright color to match the flowers. The blue will barely be noticeable."

Olivia studied the girl's reflection. "It occurs to me that we are much the same size although you are more slender. And I have more gowns than I will ever possibly use. Will you not allow me to give you one—lend it, if you prefer? It would make me so happy. Truly it would."

"But it's not necessary," Tish replied brightly. "Your clever alterations and suggestions have saved the day. Now I shall change out of my finery and take this garment home. To air, to air, to air," she laughed. "And then I shall walk to Kendal and see what the shops have to offer. Roses bloom in so many shades, it will be easy to match a length of silk."

Olivia was still not convinced, but another fifteen minutes of Tish's exuberance finally satisfied her doubts. When the friends said good-bye at last, it was with excited promises to meet again the next day and exchange news of the coming festivities.

Her arms folded on her updrawn knees, Tish buried her head. She could not face Olivia today, not and maintain that happy mask. The truth was that a full day and night hanging in front of an open window had only reduced the moth odor a minute fraction. Forty years building, it would never disappear entirely. It would not do. She would be equally charming draped in the linen sheet on the grass before her.

She grimaced. In the novels lent her by the rector's daughter—and she read them almost compulsively these days —there was always an ingenious but ready solution to the heroine's woes. A curtain that could be cut into an elegant dress so becoming that the heroine was transformed. Ugly duckling to swan. And the hero—a tall man, of course, with thick black lashes and a proud nose bent ever so slightly; an impatient man, an overly proud man—would take one look . . .

Scrambling to her feet, Tish pressed her hands against her hot cheeks. What fustian! As if she cared a twig about the ball. As if she were so lost to pride that she would borrow a gown from Olivia. Let *him* dance the night out with Lady Regina Douglas, her and her sugar-sharp tongue. Him and his precious horse and toplofty manners.

Tossing her head as though to shake off all foolish thoughts, Tish ran down the hill. Grand-père was keeping to his bed today. The heat, he said, had given him the toothache. She would read to him for an hour or two from those French treatises on science. Nothing so eased his mind as that. And then she would coax him to lend her Bowen's services for just half a day. She must get on with her plans. As if she worried about ball gowns or such fripperies when there were plans to be made. Adventures to try!

Silence was all-enveloping. There was still little breeze and the motion of the small rowboat was almost imperceptible. With a mischievous twinkle, Tish slipped off the heavy clogs and blue stockings in one gesture. She stretched her toes luxuriously. Why couldn't one stay young forever? Or at least, she thought, not have to do what is "proper for a young lady." As a child she had run barefoot the whole summer long.

Abandoning clogs and stockings in the boat, she lugged a large stone to secure the boat's anchor, then turned and ran as fast as she could across the bank and up onto the moor, a wide field full of white foxgloves. When she finally collapsed, out of breath, the tiny, bell-like flowers were as soft as eiderdown only cooler. She yawned. She must get up and gather the berries. Reading until late in the night had taken more of a toll than she realized, however, and before she knew it she was fast asleep.

Judging by the sun, it was more than two hours later when she awoke. A nice nap. Stretching, she peered around for the basket she needed to hold the strawberries. A grin broke across her face as she realized she'd forgotten to bring it. Where was her mind these days?

A sudden noise shattered the bucolic tranquillity and sent her scrambling to her feet. Straight ahead, not more than twenty yards away, stood the one creature in the world that Tish feared. A cow. And it was a giant cow, truly the largest and meanest-looking beast she had ever seen, with a ghostly, menacing white face.

With a startled shriek, she bolted toward a tree. The cow

stood between her and the lake, and she imagined it charging straight at her, to butt her with that massive head! She reached desperately for the lowest tree limb and managed to pull herself up, ignoring the burning scrape of her hands on the rough bark as she climbed farther and farther. Only when she was as high as possible did she stop. Her heart was pounding loudly in her ears and it seemed about to burst. Screwing her eyes tightly shut, she forced herself to slow her ragged breaths.

Fully five minutes elapsed before she felt sufficiently calmed to open her eyes and look down for the blasted thing. Then another shock sent her heart thumping again, a hammer against her ribs. She had an audience of two. One was chomping placidly on tufts of grass at the base of the tree. The other was grinning wickedly.

"Good afternoon, Lady Letitia," Lord Ardenly made a deep bow. Then, without another word, he swung himself with ease up into the tree and settled on the limb by her side. "Perhaps you might move just an inch or two toward the trunk," he suggested. "I am not totally confident that this branch can withstand our combined weight."

"Then you might move," Tish said icily.

"Oh no." His smile was pleasant. "You have chosen by far the nicest perch of all. I wouldn't be satisfied elsewhere."

Muttering under her breath, Tish leaned forward to slide over but her skirt snagged on a jagged stump and she found herself caught tight. When she yanked the material loose a long rent opened, revealing her white petticoat. Now thoroughly enraged, she clambered recklessly onto a farther branch, a slim one that shuddered precariously with each movement.

"I can't say you've made a safe move, but I will certainly be more comfortable now," Ardenly commented with that same cool smile. He arranged himself against the tree trunk. "Lovely view, eh?"

"If you would chase that beast away," Tish snapped, "I would get down."

"Really? Afraid of a cow? The redoubtable Lady Letitia? I find that hard to credit."

"It isn't necessary that you believe or disbelieve," she fumed, "just chase away that cow. Now."

"Seems you have the custom of getting into predicaments and then demanding assistance," Alec said thoughtfully. "If you choose to make a cake of yourself, my dear, you must suffer the consequences."

"Are you or are you not going to chase that beast away?"

"Not," he grinned. "I am quite tired and a little rest will do me good. Besides, I like the perspective." His eyes lingered on her bare feet.

"Please chase the cow away."

He ignored that to ask, "Aren't you curious about why I'm here?" Observing the darkening of Tish's deep brown eyes and the mutinous set of her shoulders, Alec didn't wait for a reply.

"I was out walking, you see. As you observed early in our friendship, there is precious little else to do in this place except walk. So I was walking. And my attention was caught by a rowboat drawn up on the shore of the lake and nary a sign of its occupant. I thought I'd have a look around and frankly, dear child, if that cow hadn't startled you awake I might have done so myself by stepping on you." He chuckled, "You do have the damnedest way of appearing out of nowhere. Almost magical. Are you magical?"

She blushed fiercely and refused to meet his searching look. She was suddenly aware that in addition to looking a fool for climbing a tree to escape a cow, she was barefoot, her skirt torn, her elbows and hands skinned and dirty from her frantic climb, and her hair was hanging in a tangle of foxgloves and leaves. She wondered wildly if it were possible to faint on purpose. Surely he wouldn't let her fall out of the tree? If only she could faint and wake to find herself at home and him someplace else, someplace where he couldn't stare at her with that strange questioning smile. She tried holding her breath, a trick he regarded at first with a quizzical lift of one brow. She noted with interest that his wry amusement soon changed to alarm and at the same time the green leaves around him began to blur in the oddest way. The shocks of the day were proving too much even for the stalwart Letitia and part of her wish, at least, was coming true. She was about to faint.

"Wake up, love. There's a good girl."

Next thing she knew her head was against Ardenly's shoulder and she was half-lying on the ground. Her lids felt too heavy to move.

"Wake up, Tish. Wake up," he repeated anxiously. He searched her face. In the setting sun she was both childlike and seductive and he couldn't resist brushing her forehead with his lips.

"Thank God," he whispered as her eyes fluttered and opened.

"I'm awake," she announced unnecessarily.

"Do you feel all right? I caught you in time but . . ."

"I'm fine," she insisted, struggling to sit, but he held her back.

"You'll faint again if you get up too rapidly."

"I won't. Though why I should have done so before I cannot imagine." Her voice was clear and strong and he looked at her suspiciously.

"You didn't just wake, did you?"

The deepening stain of red on her cheeks confirmed his suspicion.

"It doesn't make any difference," she squirmed.

"Oh, no?" he tightened his grip. "I think it does. As the Bard says, 'The summer's flower is to the summer sweet, though to itself it only live and die.'"

"What does that have to do with your kissing me?" she asked without thinking.

"Little enough," he chuckled, "except that I'm glad you were awake. You smell of flowers," he murmured against her hair, "summer flowers and you feel so—so alive." Cradling her in his arms, he pulled her down to the soft grass.

"You are a lake witch," he whispered, "and you have bewitched me. It *is* magic. I can't keep you out of my thoughts."

Hypnotized by his eyes, so strange with elusive flashes of brown and green, Tish couldn't pull away. His embrace was fierce and comforting. She shivered.

"I shouldn't be here with you, Alec. We both know it."

"Are you cold, Tish? Or frightened? You mustn't be afraid of me. I only want to kiss you once. Once," he smiled tenderly, "when I know you're awake. I know I promised I wouldn't. May I kiss you, summer-sweet Tish? Just once?"

Tish nodded. There could be no other end to this extraordinary day.

"May I kiss you?" he insisted.

"Yes," she said waveringly. "Please."

He burst into laughter at that, his arms tightening so hard around her that she grew breathless and could hear his heart beat. It was a deep, joyful sound.

"You are magical," he exulted, "you are different from any woman I've ever known." He bent his head and captured her mouth.

A shaft of moonlight, breaking over the hills, was like a whip against her senses. She tried to push Alec away, but he was lost in the passion of the moment.

Finally he drew a deep breath and their lips parted. "I— forgot myself. Forgive me." His voice was muffled but not angry. "I'll be back in a moment." He strode off toward the water where he knelt and bathed his face.

Then, a gentle hand lifted her chin up so that she had to

look up at Alec. "I understand how you feel," he said gently. "I hope you will forgive me. It won't happen again." He gave a low, bitter laugh. "I make promises to you and then break them, it appears. But not this time."

"There's nothing to forgive," she said tremulously. "It just happened."

His jaw tightened and he looked past her. "Won't they be concerned about you at home?"

"No." She tried to smooth her very wrinkled, torn skirt. "I'm often out all day."

He smiled. "You're a free spirit, Letitia Abbott. A creature of your beloved mountains and lakes. I can't picture you anywhere else." He looked away to stare blankly at the horizon.

"Shall we go?" Tish suggested timidly. "Even for me, it's getting late."

"Yes. Sorry, my mind was wandering. I'll row you back, if I may."

"And you won't say anything?"

"Say anything?" his eyes flashed dangerously.

"I mean about the cow and the tree."

His expression cleared. "Oh, that. It's our secret, my dear." Then he added with a chuckle, "I wouldn't have missed it for anything. The sight of you shooting up off the ground and into the tree!"

"And you scrambling up after me like a schoolboy." She giggled.

The sound of their mirth joined the other night sounds on the moor and lasted well after they had crossed the lake.

CHAPTER 10

The charm and surprise of the twelve follies and the elegance of Lansdale Hall had the effect Lady Margaret had anticipated, and she was literally purring. Gliding through the crowded rooms to inspect, greet and observe, she found nothing to fault. She herself was at her best, the somberness of her black silk gown relieved by the famous Lansdale parure: square-cut emeralds set into a tiara, necklace, rings and bracelets. So large were the jewels that one might have expected her insubstantial figure to collapse under their weight, but if they were burdensome, it was a burden she carried effortlessly.

The air was redolent of perfume, cosmetics and flowers. Massive vermeil urns spilled orchids onto the tables. Later the smells of cigars and snuff, brandy and food would mingle in. Conversation was slightly hushed. After a few dances and several glasses of ratafia or punch, the hum would grow much louder. As, indeed, the music would of necessity get louder and faster. "Too many slow dances late in the evening," the conductor was wont to mutter, "and older guests fall asleep standing up!"

The finery of the guests was dazzling. The ladies' hair was elaborated by corkscrew ringlets, feathers, flowers, ribbons, jewels, turbans and more. Current fashion allowed extensive displays of the female bosom as necklines were, in general, very décolleté and materials were the lightest possible, sometimes so transparent that it was necessary to wear white or pink tights for a modicum of modesty. The ladies were better dressed by far for the tropics than for the chilly District's nights but they were saved from pneumonia by the current passion for shawls, especially shawls from Cashmere, and these draped gracefully across their shoulders or lay close by on chairs in the event that mesdames felt a chill.

The gentlemen, on their part, were just as colorful, affecting primary colors in any combination. A crimson waistcoat, blue jacket and pink breeches were not out of order. English tailors were unrivaled the world over for stretching cloth so that it fit like a second skin. The snugger the fit, the more correct the dandy.

Everything, Lady Margaret concluded, was as it should be. George was a son to be proud of—handsome and distinguished. She found him in the gold-and-rose drawing room with a circle of friends. He looked happy, she noted. Happier than he had since he came home.

"Excuse me, Lady Lansdale." It was Regina, a vision in diaphanous white with silver ribbons and blood-red roses in her curls. "I must compliment you on your party. It is certainly the most elegant event of the year."

"Thank you, my dear. But how is that you are not dancing? When I looked into the ballroom it seemed you were besieged by every eligible man there."

"You would not have ineligible guests, ma'am," Regina smiled. "I have been enjoying your superb orchestra—such a large group—but I wanted to pay you my compliments."

"Very prettily done, child." She eyed her sharply. Even as they spoke, Regina was scanning the drawing room, obviously searching for someone.

"If it is George you want, he was by the fireplace in the drawing room only a few moments ago."

"What?" Regina turned back. "I beg your pardon."

"I suggested that if it is George you are looking for," Lady Margaret said archly, "he is in the drawing room."

"Oh, no, no. I was merely admiring the effect of the flowers. And . . . and your gown. Stunning."

The older woman smiled faintly. "Another pretty compliment, and one which I can return. White becomes your fairness. But see here, the widowed Duke of Fergusson is bearing down upon us with a look in his eye that suggests he spies a possible duchess. It would not do to snub him."

And although the widower in question was portly and beyond the first flush of youth, Regina dimpled prettily when he asked her to dance and allowed herself to be led away.

Lady Margaret chuckled. "A fair catch but not the one she wanted, I dare say."

She entered the dining room, and a cluster of Lansdale cousins, noses uniformly elevated, looked the other way. "Dead bores all," she grumbled under her breath.

Seeing Mrs. Follett, the rector's wife, standing alone by a towering confection of whipped cream and fruit, she looked around for someone to whom she could introduce her. Insignificant as the woman was on the social scale, and dowdy as well, she could not be left standing alone. She spied Lord Atheneum, a windbag who cultivated eccentricities to capture attention. This past year he had adopted a preference for yellow and had had his town house redecorated and his wardrobe redone in that one color, going so far in his zeal as to eat only yellow fruits and vegetables. A bore also, Lady Margaret judged, but a man who was determinedly charming to everyone. He'd do splendidly. Within minutes, as she intended, the match had been made and the rector's wife was dancing with the possessor of one of the oldest titles in England and enjoying herself enormously.

Outside, halfway down the curving drive, Hugh and Olivia chatted animatedly as they waited for carriages before them to disgorge their occupants so that they, too, might draw up to the front door. The third member of their group, Tish, was silent.

"I can't think why you've been a hermit lately," Hugh said to her. "Liv should have seen to it." He looked at his sister reproachfully.

"I did send several notes to Tish, Hugh. I told you that before."

"Still, she ought to have come." His earnest, open face was clouded. "After all, she's George's good friend. We're the newcomers. And we've been in the thick of all the fun."

"George has inquired about you constantly," Olivia reminded Tish.

"He could have come himself," she answered stiffly, "rather than sending a groom with invitations."

"Lord Lansdale has been rather busy," Olivia suggested.

"I'll say he's been busy!" Hugh exploded. "Last weekend we fellows went north to the Eden River. Salmon fishing. You can't imagine the size of them." He shook his head in wonder. "One Lord Ardenly—Alec—caught was as large as this." He stretched both long arms to their widest. "And he had a dozen nearly that big."

"My brother has found himself a hero in Lord Ardenly," Olivia teased.

"Sure have. Look, Liv, the fellow is a crackerjack shot, a first-rate fisherman, and the most monstrously good hand at faro I've ever seen. Handles the ribbons—I can't tell you, but it's something to see. I don't know what the fellow doesn't do better than any man here. Anyway," he grinned, "you've found yourself a bit of a hero in that friend of Alec's from London, that John Campbell."

Blushing prettily, Olivia hushed him and turned to Tish. "It hasn't all been for the gentlemen. They joined the ladies for a picnic by the lake. Very pretty. And last night there was a lamb shearing and a country party after." Her eyes twinkled and she smiled at Hugh for affirmation. "It was a sensation. There were fiddlers from Ambleside and we all danced in the barn. And I know George sent you a note about it."

"Yes," Tish looked away.

"At least you're here tonight," Olivia said softly, "and this is the most important party. Although we seem to be an age arriving."

Craning his head out the window, Hugh pronounced, "Just three more in front of us. What a jam! Worse than the afternoon press in Hyde Park."

For Tish, the wait was too short. She dreaded the moment when she would see him, Hugh's hero, the Nonpareil, the Earl of Ardenly.

Tish had resolved not to come to the ball. She had no gown, for one thing, and her pride would not let her turn to Olivia. More importantly, the memory of her experience on the moor haunted her. The first night she had tossed in her bed, sleepless, haunted with shame at the way she had responded to Alec's embrace. But even a fitful night's sleep restored some common sense and thereafter she tried to view the event with detachment, with perspective and common sense. She had kissed him back. Nothing more. Nothing shameful. Except that Tish had never been kissed in her entire life, and her response, her pleasure, astounded and alarmed her. She couldn't face Alec until she sorted out her feelings. Then day after day passed without a word from him and each day she grew more confused.

Out of the welter of her emotions, she had at last to admit one certain truth. She loved him. She loved him, had loved him even before that night, perhaps from the moment she fell into his arms from the balloon. No, not then, that was romantic nonsense. She didn't know when it happened. He had laughed at her jokes, understood her moods and her mind, argued with her as though she were a worthy opponent. She loved him. And it was hopeless. They were unsuited in every way and there was no future in it.

Like a patient who has survived a serious illness, she shakily considered her life from a new perspective. Why did he stay away? She found a dozen explanations, each worse than the one before. Perhaps he guessed that she loved him and was horrified. He was fearful of entrapment! Her tormented imagination was limitless. Perhaps he was in love with Lady Regina. Perhaps they were engaged. Perhaps he had returned to London and would never return. Perhaps he had fallen from a crag and broken his leg. His neck. Perhaps he was dead!

When more than a week elapsed with no word, she swallowed her pride and went to visit Olivia. She found little comfort there but she did learn that Ardenly wasn't dead, wasn't gone, and wasn't, so far as Olivia knew, engaged. She still didn't know why he hadn't come to see her.

Pride and chagrin battled desire and lost. Taking a deep breath, Tish had blurted out, "I have no gown, Olivia. May I borrow one of yours to wear to the ball? Anything. Please."

"Of course," Olivia had beamed. "And I have just the thing. It will be perfect on you." She pulled from the wardrobe a gown of fern-green Italian crepe. The bodice was severely plain, cut low, and the skirt, instead of falling straight, flared slightly at the hem, as was the newest style, with a single row of ruffles at the hem.

"You aren't the frilly type, Tish, and this gown might have been designed with you in mind. Here, slip it on."

"It's warmer than silk," Tish whispered, running her fingers over the soft, crinkly fabric.

Both girls studied the pier glass with relief. "It needs taking in just a bit all the way down," Olivia mused. "You are slimmer than I. But the style is extremely becoming."

Tish regarded her reflection with astonishment. She was slim, graceful and poised. "Almost a transformation," she chuckled.

"What colors did you wear in London?" Olivia asked, studying her carefully. "I cannot believe you weren't a sensation if you appeared like this."

"I wore white. And pale blue and pale pink. That's what all the girls wore their first season, according to my cousin. And she was right for the most part. But I look hag-ridden in sherbet shades and ridiculous in white with ruffles and ribbons. I knew something was wrong with the way I dressed, but I didn't know what." She grinned broadly. "I wonder if my cousin advised me badly on purpose?"

"Tish!" Olivia objected. "How can you suggest such a thing?"

"Hmmmm. Their daughter was only passably good-looking and hadn't a brain in her head. Compared with me in my revolting pinks, however . . . Who knows? It doesn't matter." She smiled at her image.

"And what about your hair?"

"It won't curl."

"I remember. What about braids?"

Ignoring her horrified protest, Olivia pushed Tish to a stool and began to brush her long hair. "How soft your hair is," she murmured, "and thick. Now let's see, one long braid plaited in a circle high up at the back of your head, a few loose tendrils over your ears. Yes, perfect. Different, yet becoming."

Tish started nervously. Hugh, leaning into the carriage, was tapping her repeatedly on the arm. "We've arrived, fair lady," he was saying gaily. Olivia was behind him on the stairs.

Taking three deep breaths, Tish adjusted the tiny reticule around her wrist and allowed him to hand her down.

The first person she saw was Alec. He stood near the doorway, his head inclined to hear the man at his side, his eyes riveted on the entrance. His serious expression did not change when he saw her, but he immediately straightened, patted his companion on the back and walked toward her.

"May I have the honor of the first dance?" He made a small bow. Only when he turned to greet Olivia and Hugh did he smile, and even then his eyes remained grave.

Tish's chin went up and she forced herself to smile. "Hugh has spoken for my first dance," she said proudly.

There was a flicker of something in his expression and he hesitated.

"I don't believe you've met John," Olivia broke in. "He's only arrived these past five days. This is Lady Letitia Abbott, John. May I present John Campbell."

A sandy-haired man with a wide smile and a pleasant Scottish brogue pumped her hand enthusiastically. "I'm glad to meet you. Olivia thinks the world of you."

Lady Margaret came up just then to the group and in the flurry of greetings, Tish felt a strong hand at her waist propel her away.

"Lord Ardenly, this is outside of too much," Tish sputtered. "I told you I am promised to Hugh for this dance."

"I would not provoke a quarrel," he advised her coolly. "It would create an unpleasant scene. And you needn't fear Hugh's wrath. I spoke with him earlier and he ceded me his place."

Holding herself as far away as she could, Tish stared resolutely at his cravat.

He gave her a little shake. "It's your turn to contribute to the conversation, ma'am. Such as, 'How nicely you waltz, m'lord,' or 'What fine weather we're having.' You would not scandalize society by staying mum?" He chuckled and pulled her, despite her resistance, closer. He was an excellent dancer, light on his feet despite his size, and she felt her treacherous body relax in his embrace.

"That's better," he whispered against her brow. "One thing more, has my valet done damage to my jacket that you cannot tear your eyes away? I shall dismiss him at once."

Tish giggled, her lively sense of humor betraying her. "Gammon! Your tailor and your valet are impeccable, my lord, as are you. And you know it."

"I am relieved to hear it. Won't you forgive me then for stealing Hugh's dance? I couldn't remain at the front door much longer, you know. Half the guests already think I am the butler."

She glanced up and found him smiling warmly down at her. "You aren't dignified enough to be the butler," she smiled. A slight frown creased her wide brow. "How did you come to be there?"

"Can't you guess?" He raised her hand, brushing it against his mouth. "I was waiting for a naïve forest creature," he murmured, her fingers muffling his words. "A mysterious, bewitching enchantress in green." He laughed softly. "I knew you would dance divinely, Tish. I knew it." And he whirled her faster and faster.

Tish, content in his arms, gave herself over to the pleasure of the dance, her steps perfectly matching his.

For several minutes they turned in harmony but then it became too much: the crescendo of the lilting music, the contrasting shadows and flame from the long wax tapers, the force of his presence, and the volatile rise and fall of her emotions. Tish stumbled and would have fallen but for the two arms that sprang around her.

"I'm sorry," she gasped, collapsed against him.

"You need air," he muttered. "We both do." And being Ardenly, he managed somehow to get her through the crowded ballroom without anyone taking notice of her sad state.

A dozen couples were strolling on the wide veranda overlooking the valley. Alec hurried her by, not stopping until they were well away from the crowd. A marble bench under a grape arbor provided the privacy he sought.

"Better?" he studied her anxiously.

She nodded and gave an embarrassed laugh. "I have always scorned women who succumb to the vapors. I'm not like that. It's just that I am sadly out of practice, both with waltzing and with being in such a crowd. If you'd like to return to the house, please do. I—I think a turn in the garden . . ."

"Tish! I want to be with you. There, dancing, or here. Better here." His voice deepened. "Don't you understand me?"

She deliberately turned away. "The party is very gay," she said brightly.

"Don't be a dunce," he scolded softly.

"A dunce!" she bristled. "Since I have not had the pleasure of your company for days," she said pointedly, "I could not possibly know what is in your mind."

"Aha. The wood nymph unsheaths her thorns."

"Fustian!" she snapped. "I've had enough air, thank you, Lord Ardenly, and wish to return to the ballroom. After all, I have not even greeted my hostess properly on account of being practically dragged out of the room."

He drew in a sharp breath. "Heaven save me, Tish, but you are acting the pea-brained goose and it is more than I can bear." He ran his fingers impatiently through his hair and stood abruptly. "I waited for you by the front door like a moonstruck calf, madam, and what's more, I told you so. Now if that don't show you something, I've been mighty wrong about you. I wanted to see you, dammit, to talk to you. Do you want to see me or not?" he thundered.

"Yes," she gulped. She caught her lower lip between even, white teeth and admitted that she did, truly, want to see him.

"Good." He bent down and swung her up into his arms.

"Put me down," she implored. "Someone will see us."

"Do you come willingly?" he growled.

"Of course. Idiot," she chuckled. "Put me down."

"Good." Setting her down, he pulled her after him toward the lower gardens, away from the house.

"Ardenly, is it really necessary to patrol the entire grounds at this breakneck speed?" she asked after a few minutes.

"I thought you were a walker," he retorted.

"I am," she laughed, "but not in these slippers."

Stopping abruptly, he turned on his heel to study her thoroughly, his eyes moving lazily but with a sharp gleam from the tip of her slippers to the top of her head. She felt herself blush, something she seemed to do all too often lately.

"I was so busy breaking down your icy façade, I did not say that you look very beautiful. Very, very beautiful."

"It is a pretty gown," Tish agreed nervously. "I suppose I can say so because it is Olivia's, you know. I had a—a problem with my gowns and she loaned me this. She is such a dear."

"Yes, she is, but I am not speaking of the gown. I mean *you* are beautiful. It doesn't matter what you wear. In fact," he twinkled, "in your petticoat or barefoot you are. . . ."

Plucking nervously at the fringe of her sash, Tish interrupted him. "I am not used to flirting. Or compliments."

"Then you must become accustomed to both, for I am determined to pay you a great many compliments and flirt outrageously. But come now, I shall not race but we *must* continue. I seek the perfect spot."

"The perfect spot? We've passed six or seven follies."

"Worthless. There is the Gothic ruin. No. Blazes! Is there not a single unoccupied corner in this whole place?"

They continued on in silence, he leading her by the hand. Around them couples strolled to admire the follies, laughing and stealing kisses in the shadows. The strains of music in the distance created the perfect background for romance. Even the weather had cooperated—cool but not chilly, with a bright moon and dazzling stars proclaiming no rain in sight. An enchanted land.

"Hey, my love, come out of that fog. You nearly walked into a perspiring waiter with a trayful of goblets."

Blinking hard, Tish looked around. "I was daydreaming. Or night dreaming, rather."

"I'll have none of that," Alec said with mock severity. "I want your undivided attention." They walked through an open iron gate and away from the garden, up a rather steep path. He stopped without warning, so that she collided into him. "Take care," he steadied her. "Now look around, please. We are in the perfect spot."

They had left the grounds of the estate and were in a field of sweet-smelling hay.

"The perfect spot?" Tish repeated blankly. "The fragrance is charming, I'll admit, but surely there are more scenic views than this."

"That depends upon your definition. The point, my sweet green girl, is that the perfect spot does not require a view." He cupped her face softly in his hands. "The perfect spot is one where I can be alone with you."

He was sounding almost shy, Tish thought in bewilderment. She could not credit it of Ardenly.

"Oh, Tish," he moaned, and drawing her into his arms, kissed her, softly at first, tenderly, and then with mounting passion. When he raised his head his breath was coming in jagged bursts and he could feel her trembling in his arms.

"Marry me, Tish. Be mine and let me love you as I want to."

She recoiled in surprise. "I—I don't understand."

"I'm asking you to marry me." A look of male delight warmed his eyes. She matched his passion and his love, he knew it. Tish was no simpering ice maiden. "I love you," he said softly. "I adore you and you love me. Don't deny it."

"I do love you," she said slowly.

"My darling girl," he held his arms out.

"No!" she stepped back. "No. I need to think. I never expected you would want to marry me. Not me."

He shook his head. "You must have known that night on the moor that I loved you?"

"I didn't know what to believe. You didn't come. All those days."

"I wanted to," he said roughly. "I was torn between wanting to touch you, hear you laugh, and fearing that you belong only here." He clenched his fists to keep from reaching for her.

"I wasn't sure I should uproot you from all this—" he gestured wildly. "We could visit here but my life, my business, are in Somerset and London. I have responsibilities there. At first I couldn't imagine you anywhere but here, running barefoot and free in the meadows, climbing your hills. I didn't know if it would be fair to take you away, box you up in London." He couldn't resist running his fingers down her bare arm and she shivered with pleasure at his touch.

"Even before I saw you tonight, so lovely, even before to-night I knew I had to have you. I promised myself that I would make it up to you and you have that promise. Tish," he added in a low voice, "I will love you, dearest, as no woman has ever been loved." It took all his willpower but he let his hand drop from her arm. He would not persuade her with caresses. He wanted her free choice.

"Tish," he insisted, "tell me again, do you love me?"

"Yes," she said in a small voice.

"Then marry me," he said fiercely.

"I cannot," she choked. Of course she loved him, she thought desperately. But she could not bring the shame of her family's past onto his name. And she would not burden him with her cares.

"For God's sake, Tish," he implored, "don't do this to me. Don't do this to us."

"I cannot marry you. That's the end of it."

"Cannot!" he echoed grimly. "Cannot!" Capturing her wrists, he pulled her close. His kiss was devastating, brutally forcing aside the last remnants of her inhibitions.

"Do you think mine is a conventional, biddable emotion?" he gasped, pushing her away. "Does that tell you in ways that words cannot that I love you? That I want you!" He pressed his lips together and stared at her, his eyes dazed. "I love you," he repeated. "What are you doing?"

Her mind reeling, Tish sought wildly for any excuse, any reason that would send him away. She couldn't withstand another assault on her emotions. Then she had a dreadful inspiration.

"I love you," she said, gulping back tears, "but you should not assume that my affections are yours alone."

Pale-faced and grim, he gazed incredulously at her. "Are you saying there is another man you love also?"

He did not hear her reply, the words were so faint.

"Answer me," he commanded.

"Yes, yes," she sobbed, turning blindly toward the gardens.

"You kissed me as you did on the moor and as you did tonight and you love another man!" he thundered.

"Yes," she threw back.

"Damn you," he groaned. "And damn my love for you," he said in a low voice.

Picking up the hem of her gown with both hands, Tish stumbled up the path as quickly as she could. It was impossible that the party was still in full swing, couples still dancing and laughing and enjoying themselves despite the cataclysm which had broken her heart, but they were. Catching sight of herself in a gilt-edged mirror, Tish was stunned to find that none of her inner turmoil reflected itself on her face. She was pale and wide-eyed but composed. So was Alec. He had followed her into the house and was stopping a waiter to get a glass of champagne. Catching her eye, he raised the glass in a mocking toast and downed the contents in one gulp. Then he squared his shoulders and made his way into the ballroom and straight toward the Incomparable Regina.

For the first time in her life Tish knew the bitterness of jealousy. The sight of Alec flirting openly with Regina, the charming contrast the two made—one so tall and dark and the other tiny, fair, and totally feminine—made Tish's throat constrict as though a vise were closing on it. She stared numbly from the ballroom doorway until George cut off her view and asked for a dance.

"Are you feeling quite the thing?" he asked politely when she didn't reply.

"Splendid." She raised her head. He warmed under an unusually radiant smile directed straight at him. "I would love to waltz, George, and I would especially love to waltz with you."

Bemused and delighted, he led a vivacious and sparkling Tish onto the floor.

CHAPTER 11

Tish must have tromped a full fifty miles in the two days following the ball, and this despite the almost constant downpour that soaked the countryside and battered the vegetation. Returning home only to eat, change her soaked footwear and clothes, and rest enough to partially satisfy Nanny, she always roamed north. North over bleak Kirkstone Pass and down into gentle, pastoral Patterdale, then on past the smallest of the lakes, Brothers Water, and along the bank of the long, narrow Ullswater, through a forest filled with shy red deer, past the thickly wooded shores of Derwentwater, along the beautiful valley of Borrowdale, and up to Honister Pass—the rockiest, windiest, wildest pass in the lakes.

Here she sat for hours, staring at the desolate, steep hillside falling away at her feet; sitting so immobile, so quiet, that the little Lakeland sheep forgot her presence and scrambled nimbly up the stony path beside her. From those barren heights the path drops sharply into the soft, tranquil valley of Buttermere, but Tish fixed her gaze on the steep, unwelcoming hills and the bare fells scarred with blue-gray slate quarries. Stinging hard against her cheeks, blowing back her hood and tossing the long brown hair into knots, the cold rain matched her mood.

She hoarded the fact of Alec's love. It was a fragile treasure, both precious and dangerous, and not to be sampled too frequently. For the most part she shoved the memory of his proposal to the back of her mind and thought, instead, of her family and herself. She would never be heart-whole again, but she would, she acknowledged ruefully, find satisfaction in helping her family and making a life for herself. That was cold comfort but Tish was too honest not to admit that it was, at least, a measure of comfort. And he would soon forget her in the distractions of London. That was the most galling thought of all.

She stayed out through supper the second day, huddled on the mountain pass, aching in every bone and too weary to move. The clouds scudding across the sky were so low they grazed the mountaintops. By midnight a pale moon showed fitfully and the rain lightened to a cold drizzle. The third morning dawned clear.

"The peas are beaten to the ground," Nanny was grumbling as Tish struggled up out of the covers. The old woman was clucking like an angry hen, picking up the sodden clothes that Tish had kicked off when she crawled into bed two hours earlier.

"Go way," she groaned. "Please."

"The roses," Nanny continued, "are destroyed. And I'll wager them fancy things they built up at the Hall didn't last too good either."

Tish squinted out from under the pillows. "Why are you waking me up?" she asked in a small voice.

"Your grandpa wants you." Hands on hips, Nanny regarded her critically. Her disapproval was more potent than if she had bellowed. "Not that I didn't mention you'd been out half the night like a wild thing in the dark, worrying me to death. But he took no mind. When he gets his mind fixed, nothing on the face of this earth changes it. Stubborn. Like someone else I know. 'Wake her,' says he. So I am."

She collapsed heavily onto the stool, her lined face quivering. "Bowen's working on the balloon. And I don't like it one bit."

"Ohhhh!" With a squeal of delight, Tish pushed back the blanket and threw herself down at Nanny's side, clasping the worn, hard hands in her own. She offered what consolations she could, then suddenly laughed out loud. "I've been wait-

ing so long, Nanny, and now it's here. At last it's here. Well,
partly. We're going to try another tethered ascension. There's
no danger in that, you know." She chafed the woman's hands
and smiled encouragingly up at her.

"That's your opinion," Nanny sniffled. She rose to her feet.
"At least you'll have a decent meal first," she commanded.

At the barn Nanny refused to say a word, only sniffling
audibly. Tish's grandfather, Henri de Saint-Pierre, totally ignored her and gave Tish only the briefest of greetings. His
mind was on the business ahead. The wicker basket stood
just outside the door of the barn with a tangle of ropes between it and the limp balloon, a blue-and-yellow puddle on
the damp earth. When Tish arrived, her grandfather was
poking at the ropes with his cane. He moved stiffly, apparently in considerable pain.

"Order," he muttered. "You must have them in order."

"Do sit in the chair and supervise from there," Tish
implored, shaking her head too over the confusion. "Bowen
and I will have these sorted out in no time. Please, Grand-
père, do sit."

Complaining still, he allowed himself to be led to the side.
Peering out from under bristling white brows, his eyes feverishly bright, he gave endless directions and gestured impatiently with his cane.

It was frustrating for him, Tish acknowledged, to sit by
helplessly, unable because of his crippling arthritis to take an
active role. But his constant interference was only making
progress slower. Instantly ashamed of being even the least bit
critical of her grandfather, she resolutely turned her attention
to the thick coils of rope. What a duet, she chuckled, Grand-
père muttering and Nanny sniffling.

At the sound of horses' hooves, the girl straightened like a
shot. She had looked exceedingly Friday-faced earlier when
she had seen herself in the small mirror in the hall. The
legacy of two hours' sleep was owl-dark circles around her

eyes. And handling the ropes could only have added dirt and grease to her already sad appearance. Pushing back her hair, she smoothed her skirt with hands dampened by nervous perspiration. Just when she thought her churning stomach could be repressed no longer, the horse rounded the barn and she saw, to her enormous relief, that the rider was only George. Tish fell back against the wicker basket, as drained as though she'd sprinted to Ambleside and back.

"Good morning!" George greeted her cheerfully. He stared curiously at the balloon. "Another try today?"

"Good morning," Tish smiled. "Yes, a tethered flight. How are you?"

"Recuperating. Lord, it's rigorous being a host." He grinned. "Being pleasant twenty-four hours a day and all that. But most of the crowd has departed so I can relax."

Tish bent to the ropes again. "But it was a success, wasn't it? I mean, you did enjoy yourself?"

He chuckled. "Truth to tell, I did. Don't know when I've had more fun. The ball was smashing and the hunts and all great fun. Liked showing off the old home grounds. Liked being busy."

"And how is Lady Lansdale?" Her voice was muffled as she continued to work at the ropes.

"Collapsed," he smiled, "but content. She's quite a stickler," he added proudly, "so when she puts her mark of approval, it's bound to be first-rate."

Tish worked on without comment. Finally she said nonchalantly, "I'm surprised that all your house guests have gone—I mean that they would go in the rain. Makes the roads difficult."

"Not all have gone." George jumped down and came to her side.

"Oh? Then who is left?" She laid the last coil down but still kept her gaze averted.

"Let's see. There's Hugh and Olivia. Consider them guests, though they lodge at the Inn. And John Campbell is still here. He was at Cambridge with Alec and me. Excellent chap. And Regina's stayed on. Says she'll remain another week or so. Appears the remodeling back home is lagging behind schedule." He paused and surveyed the basket and ropes with a frown. "Are you sure this contraption is safe, Tish? Don't seem a female ought to go up into the air at all, much less in such a flimsy vehicle."

"Don't you start," she snapped. "It's perfectly safe." Why on earth didn't he mention Alec, she thought angrily. If he was going to mimic Alec's obnoxious objections, he might at least mention his whereabouts.

"I don't know," George replied amiably. "Don't look very sturdy." He nudged the basket with his toe.

"Wicker is extremely strong," she said firmly. "And why shouldn't a female attempt the same exploits as a man?"

"'Tain't the same thing at all," George said reasonably. "Wouldn't expect a female to box like a man, or duel or march into battle. Or—lord, Tish, a female's supposed to paint and draw and play the piano. That sort of thing."

"That sort of thing!" she sputtered. "Well, that sort of thing doesn't satisfy me. I'm not such a ninnyhammer that I can fritter away my life in sketches and musicales." She waved her hands extravagantly. "If I didn't have my hills and lakes to roam in, and books to read, I don't know how I'd survive. And if I didn't have my ballooning to think about, I'd go mad. I have to use my mind, George, startling as that might seem."

He smiled tolerantly. They were of a height, so at least he couldn't pat her on the head, Tish thought indignantly.

"From what I know of ladies, Tish, they seem to fill an astounding number of hours in choosing silks for gowns and having their hair arranged and such fripperies. And there are children to oversee."

Tish scowled. George was hopeless, he refused to fight. And he was only aping Alec anyway. It was foolish and wicked of her to fight with George, like punching a pillow.

She swallowed her indignation and made herself smile. "From my appearance this morning you can conclude I do not linger over my toilette, my friend, like the ladies you mention. And I can't very well devote hours to children," she chuckled, "when I lack a husband."

Laughing, George agreed that children, for the present, were definitely out of the question. As for her appearance, he smiled sweetly, she always looked up to the crack as far as he was concerned.

Tish cleared her throat nervously and finally dared ask, "And Lord Ardenly? I do not recall if you mentioned him. Did you say he's left the District?"

George frowned slightly. "Yes, though I'm not clear why. He was up this morning at dawn. Went racketing back to London on such short notice that he left me only the briefest note, asking me to give my mother his apologies for his hasty departure. Said he had been called away on urgent business and didn't know when he'd return. Unlike Alec in the extreme. Usually such a stickler for manners and such."

Tish's grandfather interrupted him, inquiring fretfully whether she had completed the preparations or if she intended to moon about half the day.

"Good morning, monsieur," George bowed. "I am delighted to see you looking so well."

"I am not well," the old man answered severely. "You must forgive my granddaughter if she discontinues her conversation. She has work to do."

"Of course. I do not wish to interrupt, but I would like to learn about the process." There was no reply. "I find science fascinating," George added mendaciously.

"As you like. Bowen!" Saint-Pierre pounded the ground. "How is the furnace?"

"It goes," the farmer said cryptically.

"Bowen has been here all night," Tish explained. "The furnace cannot be left even for one moment."

George peered into the barn. "You mentioned you use old

cannons? What do they have to do with the gas that keeps the balloon up?"

"The method is simple, though slow in operation. Water, of course, is composed of hydrogen and oxygen. If steam, which is vaporized water, is brought into contact with red-hot metal, the metal combines with the oxygen to form an oxide and the hydrogen is released." She sighed at George's blank look. "Let me explain it another way. The furnace is fed with brushwood until the fire is fierce enough to turn the cannons red-hot. Actually, white-hot. These are then filled with iron turnings, water is sprayed which makes steam, and the oxygen is then left in the tubes while the hydrogen, because of its extreme lightness, passes up into a rubber tube leading to the balloon sac. When there is enough of it, the hydrogen lifts the balloon."

George shrugged helplessly and Tish tried not to sound as exasperated as she felt. "If you put a piece of paper over a fire, does it not float up?" He nodded. "*Voilà!* That is all you need to know."

"And you've already started that?" George picked up a corner of the limp balloon. "Don't look like anything is going in at all."

Tish giggled. "That's always the way. It appears empty, then the material suddenly begins to move and seemingly in a blink of an eye it begins to swell and grow until it lifts."

"This the same contraption you used when you and Ardenly—"

She turned away, checking the contents of the basket to hide her blush. "Yes," she mumbled indistinctly.

"Rope snapped. Sure that won't happen again?"

"We're using two anchor ropes this time and we're going twice as high," she said challengingly.

"Ardenly wouldn't like it." George shrugged. He forestalled her retort by turning to her grandfather. "This was your balloon in France, monsieur?"

"Indeed."

"I am full of admiration," George smiled. "May I ask how you used it?"

"I'm positive Grand-père does not wish to discuss it." Tish was suspicious of his sudden interest. It smacked of Alec's interference.

"I am very interested to learn about this new science," George persisted.

"If you are interested," the old man conceded, "there is little enough to tell. I am a scientist and as such was attracted early by the discovery of aerostation. When a French military balloon corps was formed in 1794, I offered my services. These were *ballons captifs*, you understand, to be used for observation of military movements. I was a sublieutenant in the first company of *Les Aérostatiers*."

"They had magnificent uniforms," Tish interjected proudly. "Grandfather's is preserved in the attic. Like military engineers—gold-braided tunic, epaulettes, three-cornered hat, knee breeches, and copper buttons engraved with the figure of a balloon."

"As you recall," Saint-Pierre went on quietly, "Montgolfier sent up the first balloon in eighty-two. The first manned flight was the next year. So the science was in its infancy even in ninety-four. The French are admittedly adventuresome. And putting this infant science to work for the military was great adventure.

"By 1794 the French were fighting almost every nation in Europe, but it was against the Austrians in the battle of Charleroi in Belgium that we achieved our greatest success with the balloon. The enemy were dumbfounded to see our enormous machine borne aloft with no visible means of support. The ropes, you understand, blended into the surrounding clouds. From our vantage point some twenty-one hundred feet up in the heavens we could see all—the deployment of the troops, the artillery, the ammunition wagons, even the women camp followers—spread out like toy figures on a child's map." His voice shook with excitement.

"But how did you communicate with the ground?" George asked sensibly.

"We used flag signals. Or messages written on paper and sent down with bags of sand ballast."

George ignored Tish, who was trying to motion him away. Her grandfather was normally taciturn and she feared this excited garrulousness would tire him too much. However, Saint-Pierre, stimulated by memories of the past, refused to let George go and he talked at some length with him, discussing in detail the enthusiasm of the military for their aerial spy. Even the foot soldiers shouted "hurrah" when the balloon was brought down.

Napoleon, he informed George, had been persuaded to send the balloon company along with his ill-fated expedition to Egypt. Unfortunately the first detachment was sunk at sea by a British man-of-war at the battle of Aboukir and a disgruntled Bonaparte disbanded *Les Aérostatiers* the next year—1799. Balloons and appurtenances were sold, which was how Saint-Pierre acquired his own balloon.

George scratched his head thoughtfully. "How much do you see from so high?"

"One has to be trained as an observer," Saint-Pierre answered. "Letitia will practice today."

"Fascinating," George agreed, "but it still don't seem fit for a female. That's what Ardenly said and I agree."

"Fustian!" Tish exploded. "This doesn't require strength, dear George. Not like boxing or dueling," she added. "And Lord Ardenly's opinion is hardly of interest here."

"I don't like it either," Nanny snapped.

Hushing them, Saint-Pierre studied the sky. "Good weather, not too much wind. Small, white clouds moving slowly. Shouldn't send up a captive balloon in wind," he explained to George. "A free balloon moves with the wind, but a captive one can be blown hither and thither."

"Or pitched to the ground," Bowen volunteered dourly.

"Dashed to the ground is more likely," Nanny corrected him.

"As a scientist, madam, I require accurate and ordered facts," Saint-Pierre informed her. "The air is dry, according to the hygrometer, the clouds are of the cirrus type—that is, spread about in the lofty regions and of a fibrous texture. In conclusion, conditions are favorable for an ascent."

Nanny was obdurate. "I've been a hundred feet from the house in bright sunlight and not made it back to shelter before getting soaked in a sudden thunderstorm. Now I listen to my bones. My mother and hers before her knew more than all them machines of yours. 'If red the sun begins his race, expect that rain will fall apace. The evening red, the morning gray, are sure signs of a fair day.'"

"Enough," Saint-Pierre ordered. "Meteorological phenomena are a science."

"The Lake District has its own portents," Nanny mumbled.

"The clouds of England," he parried, "are much the same as the northern part of France and those of the other parts of Europe."

"It's filling," Bowen interrupted.

They were all stunned into silence. Even to Saint-Pierre, who had seen the process many times, it was still a wonder. The balloon's envelope had been a limp sac, grimy in spots, faded and full of patches. Unimpressive. Then the material began to move slightly, ripples grew into large swells, and finally it lifted, tentatively at first, a thin pear shape, until it strained at its full height, stretched to a thirty-foot diameter. Against the clear blue sky the spherical shape was no longer a patchwork of dirty scraps but was a noble object with a beauty and almost a personality and purpose of its own.

"Unnatural, that's what it is. People got no business mixing with the birds," Nanny declared.

"I repeat, madam, it is science. A challenge to the intellect," Saint-Pierre tapped his forehead.

"Hadn't we better get on with it?" Tish asked.

"Something wrong with a man who studies clouds," Nanny concluded, "and don't even see the stars."

"Aha!" Saint-Pierre exclaimed. "You are, for once, correct. I study what is between earth and stars. The first I have known too well and the last are beyond reach. But the clouds, the atmosphere, there's a different story."

"Even the clouds are beyond *your* reach, old man," Nanny muttered under her breath.

Saint-Pierre affected deafness. The two had been squabbling over Tish for more than a decade and it was not an argument that would be settled this day. Nanny, loving Tish, wanted to protect her. Saint-Pierre, equally loving, offered her the adventure he himself would have liked to undertake.

Leaning heavily on his cane, he walked to the basket and put a large wooden case inside. "You are sure you care to make this flight? It is not necessary, you understand. I still have many experiments to make from earth. I do not require data from the air."

Tish only nodded. She had plans of her own and nothing, and nobody, would keep her from the ascension. The last two days had strengthened her resolve beyond the breaking point.

Saint-Pierre motioned to Bowen who handed him a package. "Just as ships have names," the old man said softly, "so must your craft. *Le petit oiseau*—The Little Bird." He fastened onto the basket's rim a bright blue square of cloth with a white soaring bird in its center.

Tish's eyes filled with tears as her grandfather took her hand in his and, bowing slightly, kissed it. "Very well, *ma petite*. Go safely in *The Little Bird*. I only wish I could accompany you. A glorious day lies ahead. *Bon voyage!*"

Giving Nanny and George each a hasty hug and tossing Bowen a broad grin, Tish hitched her skirt and scrambled easily into the basket. After endless waiting, she was at last under way.

So exhilarating was the moment that she let out a loud

whoop that alarmed those on the ground until she leaned out and waved. The spectators saw the balloon literally shoot up once Bowen had cast off all but the two anchor ropes that wound around the thickest beams in the barn.

The barometer recorded the rise: six hundred, seven hundred and fifty, one thousand feet, two thousand. The needle stopped as abruptly as the balloon, which was tethered as firmly at the end of the ropes as a bridled horse.

Taking a deep breath, Tish looked around. "We do not go up," she crowed, "the world has gone down!" She relaxed her tight hold of the basket's edge. Even with the mild wind there was a gentle but continuous rolling and vibration in the basket. She thanked the fates that she never suffered seasickness. A stronger wind, she realized, would cause some discomfort besides making the use of a telescope impossible.

She gave herself a small shake. She'd enjoy the panorama soon enough. First she must attend to her duties. She examined the gondola to make sure that all was as it should be. It was small, roomy enough to accommodate only three persons, made of strong yet lightweight wicker. It hung by a dozen stout ropes about five feet below the neck of the balloon. These ropes, in turn, hung from a net which covered the upper half of the balloon. The neck of the balloon was open, affording an eerie view of the blurry interior. Another rope hanging down from inside the neck was attached to a valve at the very top of the rubber sphere. Closed by springs, the valve could be operated from the basket by means of the rope. Opening the valve to allow gas to escape would, naturally, cause the balloon to descend.

The fittings in the gondola were arranged with an eye toward economy of weight and space. In order to facilitate a safe landing, there was a sort of anchor fastened to a long rope. Not that the anchor was always so useful, Tish thought wryly, recalling her first meeting with Alec. Neatly stacked wooden cases held scientific instruments with the barometer on top. Next to these was a telescope, still unopened. There

were a couple of cushions, a blanket, a large basket of food
and wine, and a half-dozen bags of sand. Throwing out the
sand, the ballast, would lighten the gondola and thus make it
rise.

Peering at the barometer, Tish reached for a notebook and
pencil to record the altitude. Exactly 2,100 feet. She found
she had gained a sense of balance and could stand and move
the two or three steps from one side of the basket to the
other without fear. She was, she realized gratefully, totally at
home in *The Little Bird*. Chuckling, she bent to extract the
thermometer. The air was pleasurably cool.

Then she couldn't resist any longer and she stood stock
still to relish the scenery. The world below was a kaleidoscope
of colors, shadings of different hues constantly shifting and
changing as the basket moved with the wind. From her aerial
perch she could see the pattern of the Lake District as never
before. It was laid out like a wheel, the hub being the high
central hills or fells, the spokes the ridges radiating away from
the hub, and the spaces between being the valleys. And it was
small. Tiny! If her balloon were truly a bird, she could cross
it herself, the whole of it from southwest to northwest, in a
leisurely hour.

Shimmering lakes among the hollows were brilliant diamond chips. The wee tarns were blue sparkles, flung down at
random. And the granite of Eskdale to the southwest was
graying pink, while beyond that the dun shades of volcanic
turf melted into the green slate of Coniston.

Tish adjusted the telescope. Beyond the gleaming lilac
water of Solway to the north, she saw the dark speck that was
Ireland on the rim of the sea. The immediate country below,
of isolated farms and button-sized villages, was crisscrossed by
gray-walled roads—steep, tortuous roads worn by Roman le-
gionnaires and medieval monks as well as Norse invaders.
Stone walls seamed mountains almost to the summits. The
vale of Grasmere directly below was on the edge of the softer,
southern landscape. To the north were ancient mountains,

grand mountains slashed by ravines and waterfalls. She could not make out the countless bridges that spanned the streams.

Scafell Pike and a dozen other pikes loomed above her craft. High as the birds she was, but not so high as they. And over all, the azure sky.

Sounds carry. Stretching luxuriously and closing her eyes to concentrate, Tish heard a dog barking, a mother calling her child. She shivered. She would never forget this day. This was solace to her bruised emotions.

The image of Alec forced itself into her peaceful thoughts. His face when she said she loved another man. His face when he put his arms around her. The security and excitement of his embrace. She sighed. When she carried out her plan, she would put herself irrevocably beyond his regard. A titled nobleman would never, could never, condescend to deal with a woman who appeared before the public on a stage, a woman who had the same low social status as an actress.

Yet that was precisely what Tish intended to become. Her family were in desperate need of money and she could think of no other scheme to assist them. She would make a balloon flight across the English Channel from Dover to France. This had been done by the Frenchman Blanchard and the American Jeffries in 1785. Seventeen years later there was another successful passage. But no woman had yet attempted the dangerous feat. Tish would do it. That in itself would cause a sensation. And then she could make money writing for the newspapers and lecturing on her flight. Lectures were highly popular; dear Olivia was testimony to that. Yes, notoriety was profitable.

Sadly, notoriety was also anathema to the *haut ton* of Tish's world. A gentleman like Ardenly might wager a fortune and race openly in his curricle from London to Bath and be roundly applauded. Applauded even if he lost that fortune. But a female of good birth was supposed to be discreet, to preserve surface appearances. She might take a dozen lovers once she was correctly married, and the whole of society might know of it, and so long as she didn't flaunt her amours publicly, it was accepted. Appearing on the lecture platform as a female aeronaut was not accepted. She would be cast beyond the reach of respectability. Even in this enlightened day a proper young lady did not submit herself to the vulgar curiosity of the crowd.

Another deep sigh escaped her lips. She did not like the prospects before her but rack her brains as she might, she could conjure up no other solution. She must earn money to support her family. The paltry pay of a governess or milliner would hardly suffice, even assuming she could subdue her outspoken character and had the talents for such employment. Really, a female of gentle birth had no choice, it was marriage or nothing. And who was there for her to marry? She could not marry Alec and foist her family and her problems onto him. She liked George far too well to marry him. Hugh? A child. No, the balloon was her opportunity, her escape. She had reconsidered her choices during her two-day vigil and there was no other way.

Shaking her head, she turned resolutely to her present duties. She must descend a few hundred feet and make observations at a lower altitude. She tugged gently at the valve rope. It resisted and she tugged harder until it snapped open and she felt the balloon drop precipitously. When the barometer read 1,600 feet, she let the valve close again and took up her notebook to record the temperature and dryness of the air.

A sudden pitch of the gondola sent the pencil flying out of her fingers and pitched her to her knees. Perhaps the air current was different at the lower level, perhaps it was the additional slack now on the anchor ropes—whatever it was, the basket began bucking like a wild horse maddened by a beesting. Tish grabbed for the basket's rim. She was too interested in the novel sensations to be frightened, but she did deem it prudent to remain kneeling. Peering over the rim, she gasped

in pleasure. She was hanging almost directly over the oval
lake in the center of the valley, and in the clear water she saw
mirrored her pitching, rolling gondola and the blue-and-
yellow balloon above it, undulating first to one side and then
the other. Also reflected was the cerulean blue sky and dark,
ominous clouds on the edge of the image. She looked up.
Yes, the sky was darkening, presaging a storm.

She strained for the valve rope but it was just out of reach.
On her knees still, she inched forward, one hand still tightly
clinging to the basket's rim, the other stretched out toward
the elusive rope. Suddenly the stack of wooden boxes slid
across the floor, one banging hard against her thigh. The barometer fell with a crack and the basket of food skittered
back and forth.

Grimly she forced her hand out farther and farther until she
managed to catch hold of the valve rope. It wouldn't move.
The valve was jammed. It hadn't worked easily before, and
now it seemed to be stuck. Meanwhile the gondola was tossing about like a rowboat in the midst of an Atlantic gale! Up
the side of a forty-foot wave, bouncing tremulously on the
crest, and then shuddering down the steep incline into the
trench below.

Gritting her teeth, Tish yanked as hard as she could on the
rope. She had to descend or she might be thrown out of the
basket altogether. What could be the matter? She and
Bowen had checked and rechecked the apparatus yesterday.
Her brow wrinkled. They hadn't checked it this morning. But
what could have happened during the night?

"He was up this morning at dawn. Went racketing back to
London . . ."

George's words rang in her ears. Instinctively she continued to pull and tug but her attention was riveted on that
statement. Would Alec have caused a malfunction in the
balloon to prevent the flight? And then have left to avoid
suspicion? He was, after all, adamant in his conviction that

women had no business with ballooning. What other explanation was there? Nonsense. Malfunctions were commonplace. A hazard of the game.

All at once the valve rope responded. Every other consideration fled as she estimated the rate of fall and checked the escape of the gas. It wouldn't do to hurtle down so fast she would be dashed against the ground!

Automatically Tish went through preparations for landing. She propped sandbags and cushions nearby to soften the shock. One hand grasped the basket's edge and the other secured the precious instruments. They must not be destroyed. At the last moment she held still to the boxes but let go of the rim and lifted the anchor onto the ledge. Then, when she saw the treetops coming up fast, she hurled the anchor with all her strength into the tangle of branches already scratching against the wicker sides. More shudders, strong jerks, and the basket was caught tight, the anchor twisted around the trunk of a sturdy sycamore.

The sudden descent caused a peculiar sensation in her ears, but otherwise Tish was unharmed. A bumpy landing, she conceded, but a safe one. As though they were still at a great distance, she heard Bowen and George shout faintly from the other side of the meadow. Slight deafness from the rapid descent would not last long. She felt removed from them, in another sphere, as she watched them run toward her. She would probably feel removed, she realized, for days and days. She had visited the realm of birds and clouds and she could hardly expect to be exactly the same ever again.

CHAPTER 12

"You just might want to consider going a step or two up shore," came the lazy drawl. "I believe the ground there is less pitted with pebbles."

Tish whirled. It was Ardenly, handsome and dark as a devil, sprawled on the ground not ten feet away, regarding her with a lazy grin.

"How—how dare you!" she sputtered indignantly. "Did you come here to spy on me?"

In answer, he pulled a gold watch from his vest pocket and flicked up the cover with his thumbnail. "I am not in the custom of making assignations at . . . at six-fifteen in the morning." He snapped it shut. "And I do not mean to be unflattering, madam, but I could not possibly expect to find you here, now could I? Unless you are an habitual early swimmer and I a round-the-clock Peeping Tom?"

The impudence of the man, Tish fumed. He had allowed her to pull her skirt half over her head before speaking. She blushed, recalling that this was the second occasion on which the Earl of Ardenly had viewed her in her petticoat.

"Please don't let me interfere with your bathe," he continued pleasantly. "As I said, the ground a bit farther along is smoother. Much more comfortable for bare feet."

Tish's eyes flew to her toes. "How dare you allow me to—to disrobe," she muttered. "Why didn't you speak earlier?"

His chuckle grated worse than any insult. "Dear me, you feel this is not quite *comme il faut*, as you might say?"

"What are you doing here?" she demanded, coloring a deeper red under his coolly amused regard.

The black eyebrows quirked and he gave a small shrug. "It was too much, I suppose, to expect you to welcome me back with flowery phrases." He waited but she made no response. "I returned last night." He grinned. "Did you miss me?"

At a loss for a suitably scathing retort, Tish looked away. That he should return and find her like this, as always, exhibiting a woeful lack of decorum. Lady Regina would never in a thousand years steal down to the lake at dawn, barefoot, to bathe in her slip. Damn him. And then, quite unbidden, popped into her head the fleeting wish that she were in a wildly flattering red bonnet and gown. So flattering she would stun him with her beauty. She grimaced impatiently. What fustian. He was not only not stunned, he was amused, acknowledging her discomfort with an avuncular smile. It must have been momentary madness that prompted his declaration at the ball. There was no tenderness in his expression now, nothing to hint of the lover. Only amusement and, perhaps, a shade of condescension.

"A gentleman would apologize and depart at once, leaving a lady to her privacy."

The brown-green eyes glinted and he gave a shout of laughter. "Once again you come acropper on your own doing and then demand that *I* back away. Will you never learn my nature? I am not persuaded that you should be master where you and I are concerned," he went on more softly. "You want a strong hand, my sweet shrew."

"I am not a—a mare!" she exploded. "The only thing I want is a view of your back as you walk away from me. Immediately."

Another laugh exploded from his mouth. "I must be mad," he gasped between chortles, "I believe I even missed your sharp tongue these ten days. You'll be astounded to hear, my dear, that I even missed your beloved mountains. At first I was truly drugged with the familiar stench of London and the sight of the dingy veil of smoke hanging over the city."

He laughed again at her look of outrage. "Yes, Tish, the familiar is precious and the foul air of London is familiar.

"I virtually leaped out of bed each morning to feast my eyes on the jumbled skyline of towers and cupolas, to hear the oaths of street vendors, to inhale the stench of the coal air. But look at me, just one night back and I am up beforetime to admire the scenery. You have converted me to a love of mountains, small mountains." His eyes narrowed, and he studied her curiously. "Is it possible that your sleep is troubled, Tish, as mine is? Is that why you quit your bed so early?"

She fidgeted uncomfortably under his gaze. She had dismissed her suspicions of Alec sabotaging the balloon as nonsense, but she couldn't resist probing. "We—we made another ascension."

"George told me."

"I am in one piece, as you see."

"I did not predict your immediate destruction," he answered. "The next trip may also be a safe one. And the trip after that. But I did say, and I truly believe, that inevitably there will be an accident and you will be hurt. And that is why you should leave such antics to the stronger sex."

"Ridiculous," she flashed.

He raised his hand in weary protest. "Let's not hash that out again." He rose to his feet. "The topic is obviously exhausted. Certainly I have done with it. I would rather learn why you are so determined to do this thing. What is your motive? You are uncommonly stubborn in character, that is plain, and this *idée fixe* of yours has deep roots. But why this particular idea? And I ought to warn you that I am not totally ignorant of your circumstances."

She colored guiltily and lowered her eyes. "I don't know what you mean."

"Yes you do. There is a mystery in your household, my dear. And I don't like mysteries. Tell me," he took a step toward her, "why you must persevere with the ballooning? And what is wrong with your mother? Can't you trust me?" he added with a sweet smile.

Dawn's pink light spilled over the hills into the cup of the valley.

Feeling a desperate desire to lay her head on his strong shoulder, to confide all, Tish looked around wildly. "There's . . . there's no mystery," she faltered.

"Trust me. Please." He held out a hand to her.

"No! No!" she protested. "There's no mystery. I—I balloon because I like it. And you—you lack the courage to try it yourself so you would deny the chance to me. Perhaps you even tried to ensure my failure by damaging the apparatus!" The moment the words were out she regretted them. Whatever he was or was not, Alec was an honorable man. Frightened by her own accusation, she trembled to see the taut fury it evoked.

With one long stride he was at her side, grasping her arm in an iron grip. "If you were a man, I'd whip you," he said grimly. "No one has ever made such an accusation to me. No one."

"I—I judge by the evidence," she stuttered hysterically.

He dropped her arm as though it were a poisonous snake. "You have reminded me before that you are long out of the schoolroom," he said icily, "yet your behavior is closer to the nursery. Your vision is very limited, ma'am, and you are too rustic and immature—despite your great age—to be aware of it. Even by your own standards, however, I pass the test of courage." He turned away and took a few steps before looking back at her. His eyes were cold and contemptuous.

"This very afternoon we are embarked on an eagle hunt. As I understand the matter, this is as dangerous as any endeavor in these parts and yet is a necessary hunt as the golden eagle is a terrible predator on sheep and dogs. One man is lowered by a rope, as you know, to pluck the eagle's eggs from the nest. Slightly dangerous," he finished sarcastically, "if the mother should return precipitately. Although one does have an ice ax for protection. And the honor has fallen to me."

Tish stared wide-eyed after his retreating back. When would she learn to control her tongue and not let it rattle on, victim to her emotions? Tears started to her eyes. "Rustic and immature. Nursery." So must she seem, so she had behaved. And now what danger was Ardenly in?

It was the longest day of her life.

By nightfall, Tish was wild. She had stormed into the kitchen so often to peer at the oak clock in the corner that Nanny banished her from the room, complaining that her cake had fallen in the oven and the butter curdled in the churn because of the door slamming over and over. Saint-Pierre, suffering from a severe arthritis attack, had taken to his bed and refused visitors. A note arrived from Olivia asking Tish to dinner at the White Lion Inn that evening, but she couldn't concentrate on the invitation and merely scribbled "no" on the paper. Too preoccupied to read, too restless to settle down to mending, she bit her nails and paced from the house to the barn and back. She dared not risk leaving the grounds, as Bowen had been one of the hunting party and she was desperate to see him.

His report, when he came at long last, was typically terse. "Went off all right," he grunted. "A good day's work."

When Tish persisted, he scratched his head and added, "He did all right. There's no knowing how long the mother will be off foraging. He got bloodied. Reckon he'll survive," he offered laconically.

With that, all sense deserted Tish and she took to her heels, racing out of the yard and up the road to Lansdale Hall. She pushed past the startled butler who responded to her furious pounding at the door and then checked, gasping, in the middle of the entrance hall. She had surprised Alec in the act of slipping a shawl around the very white, very bare shoulders of Lady Regina. And there wasn't a scratch on him.

"Good evening, Letitia," Lady Regina said graciously. She smiled, her expression holding a shade more contempt than welcome, as if it were only slightly remarkable that a caller burst in unannounced, breathless, and gaping like a deranged soul.

"We had anticipated that you might make one of our numbers this evening. Olivia made a particular point of inviting you, did she not, Ali?" She emphasized his nickname and gave Ardenly an intimate smile.

"Indeed," he drawled. After a long moment he prompted Tish impatiently, "Well? Do you join us or not?"

"No," the girl gulped. "I cannot."

"Isn't that too bad," Regina dimpled prettily. "And unfortunately George is not feeling quite the thing." She looked curiously at Alec who was frowning at Tish and then at Tish, who returned his glare with equal venom. "Nichols," Regina motioned to the butler, "please inform Lord Lansdale that Lady Letitia is here."

The granite-faced butler bowed slightly. "Very well, madam. And may I remind his lordship that your horses have been put to. I know you do not care to keep them standing."

Alec nodded curtly. "What are you doing here?" he barked at Tish.

Her head was in a whirl but she forced herself to speak slowly and calmly. "I've come to ask George how the matter proceeded today." She looked intently at the white and black marble squares beneath her feet.

"I see. Then George can give you the details. Your servant, ma'am," he said indifferently, making his bow.

The mingled scent of musky perfume and a definitely masculine spice floated behind them as Alec and Regina went out. Just as the door swung to, Alec murmured something in a low undertone that prompted a trill of delighted laughter from that lady's throat. Miserably, Tish looked around for the butler and discovered him at the foot of the wide marble staircase, motioning her to go up.

"I say, old girl, you look as knocked out as I feel." George's greeting was deflating. The light-blue eyes watched her quizzically as he entered the drawing room. Tish had drawn a footstool up to the fireplace and was huddled on it, eyes hooded by her long lashes as she looked up at him.

"Is something the matter?" He pulled a chair to her side.

"I know I look quite hag-ridden," she agreed unhappily.

"Didn't mean to offend," he said quickly. "Never think before I speak where you're concerned, Tish. Sorry if I hurt your feelings. I was surprised, that's all. You are inevitably in blooming good health."

"I'm sturdy and hardy," she said bitterly, "it's true. Not a delicate bone in my body." He made a worried noise and she smiled a little. "It's all right. You couldn't offend me if you tried, dear George. I know you mean it well. What I meant to say was that I don't think I'm in my best looks tonight either. But nothing's wrong. I've come to hear about the eagle hunt. How did it go?"

"The hunt itself was a great success. Ardenly, as always, was the hero of the day," he admitted with a grin. "Snatched four eggs from the nest without batting an eye and then gave the mama a whack or two when she tried to peck his face. It was a sight," he chuckled. "Didn't really hurt the bird, you understand, just kept her away while he retreated. Then I had to go and act the fool by falling in a creek on the way home and getting myself soaked. Took a chill."

She drew in a sharp breath. "Forgive me, I've been thoughtless, haven't I? As always. I've taken you from your bedchamber. Forgive me, please."

He pushed her back down on the stool. "Gudgeon," he said affectionately. "I don't mean to chase you away. Could do with a spot of company. Anyway, I'm not about to turn up my toes. In fact, I'd have gone to the inn tonight if my dear mother hadn't rung the peal over my head and ordered me to stay home."

She nodded absently. "Bowen mentioned something about someone, Lord Ardenly I believe, getting bloodied."

"Yes, that's right. He did get a scratch on the forehead. Nothing to it, but that portion of one's anatomy bleeds like fury. Put a bit of plaster on it and combed his hair down, à la Titus, and no one's the wiser. But how is it you aren't dining at the inn? I know the Woffingtons invited you, Hugh told me so."

"I couldn't spare the time," she said dismally. Then she recalled John Campbell and asked if he had left.

George chuckled. "Not he. Suspect he'll hang around as long as Olivia's here. Went over earlier to the inn. Made some excuse but it was clear he couldn't wait to see her."

"Or perhaps he didn't care to play the gooseberry with Regina and Lord Ardenly," Tish said sourly. "No doubt Lord Ardenly himself suggested it."

"*Lord* Ardenly? What a pucker you're in tonight, girl. What is this 'Lord' story?"

She mumbled something indistinct and sighed. "Tell me about Lord Ardenly," she said finally. "Alec, that is. Any friend of yours interests me," she added, a shade too casually, though George noticed nothing.

He declared himself pleased to oblige if she would allow him first to ring for brandy and cigars. She declined an offer of tea. "That's what I like about you, Tish," George beamed. "A fellow can be comfortable with you. Most ladies wrinkle their noses at a good cigar."

Tish waited until the footman left the room and George was settled with a decanter and glass at his elbow and a cigar that had been primed and lit. "You were going to tell me about your friend," she prompted.

"What's to say except that he's been the best friend in the world," George stated prosaically. "I had trouble at Cambridge settling in. I'd been too much to myself up here, just a tutor for male company. Had no idea where to begin, what to do. Ardenly took me under his wing, in effect." His eyes warmed as he described the past. "Taught me about buying horses, steered me into the right clubs, cautioned me about types to avoid. Introduced me to the right sort of gaming halls." He smiled at her gasp. "Lord, Tish, you can't expect a fellow to learn anything of the world without having all sorts of experiences. Ardenly ain't a loose fish but he's done his share of gambling and all the rest."

"And his family?"

"Mother died when he was a babe. Has two sisters but they're much older. Father's a cold one, to tell the truth. He and Ardenly do what they must by each other but ain't no special feeling there."

"Why would he take you under his wing at Cambridge?" she frowned. "You're the same age, yet it sounds as though he were years older."

"We're the same age by the calendar," George acknowledged wryly, "but he was ten years older in experience at that stage. He was out on his own at a young age; father didn't care what he did. Remember I was here, with mother and a tutor."

"And me," she grinned impishly.

"And you." He gazed at the fire thoughtfully. When he went on, his voice was unusually serious. "Some men just have the knack, Tish. Other men look up to them, respect them. That's Ardenly."

"And women?" she ventured timidly.

He chuckled. "Hardly any lack of those. You take a fellow with title and money and then good looks to boot, and you can be sure the gals are after him like bees to honey. Even I've had my share of hopeful mamas on my trail and I ain't half so plump in the pocket as Ardenly. Nor half so dashing, let's face it."

She squeezed his hand. "You have a considerable charm of your own, my friend."

"Thanks," he smiled. "I know I ain't no antidote. Funny thing is that it gets boring, Tish. Alec moans about it and I agree with him. All those fluttering eyelashes and agreeable ways. Confound it, Alec just looks at a female and she sets to swooning with the vapors. We've laughed over it."

"Charming!" Tish said stiffly.

"Now don't fly up into the boughs with me," George said soothingly. "You know that many's the time you and I have laughed about the marriage mart in London, the gals that have one season to catch an eligible, rich husband." She still regarded him with a stony expression and he shook his head reprovingly.

"Be fair, Tish, we've laughed about it ourselves. Alec ain't bird-witted. He can't help but notice. All I meant was that it gets tiresome. Sometimes a man wants to do the chasing."

"Chasing light skirts," she said severely.

"Now that's a subject that even I won't discuss with you," George said firmly. He stretched and poured himself another glass of brandy. "Damn pleasant here, eh, Tish?"

She rested her head on her knees, staring into the fire. "Sorry if I'm being a blockhead," she said at last. "Tell me about the war, George. And what you did . . . and Alec."

"I don't like to speak of it," George said slowly. "Truth to tell, I had nightmares for months. It's only in the last few weeks that it's started to fade."

"Please." Her large brown eyes were luminous and imploring. "Just tell me one story about Alec. Please."

"Why so curious about Alec?" George asked.

"He—because he's your friend."

"Very well." He looked at her thoughtfully. "Alec changed because of the war, I suppose. We both did, but he more than I. He had an experience that—well, it was during the Peninsular War. We served together as you know. For the first few weeks it was like playing at soldiers. Almost fun. The enemy always at a distance so that they seemed unreal. Then suddenly it became all too real. We overtook the enemy before dusk. They'd drawn up behind the Ceira River at Fez d'Aronce. Some fool commander had left their rearguard posted on our side of the river and Lord Wellington lost no time in taking advantage of their mistake. He launched a furious attack, poor devils." His voice cracked but he took a steadying breath and continued. "They retreated in such panic that half their force was left on our side of the river when they themselves blew the bridge up to protect their flanks."

Getting to his feet, he turned to look out the window at the dark valley below. His slender frame, ramrod stiff, merged into the shadows and his voice was almost disembodied, almost a whisper. "The soldiers who were cut off were desperate—they must have known their situation was hopeless. Those who did not fall to our guns drowned in a frantic, futile retreat. I myself fought in the center, always moving forward to the river through a battlefield thick with dead.

"By dusk the enemy was completely routed. I looked automatically for Alec but couldn't find him anywhere so finally I dismounted and began turning over bodies, searching for his corpse. We had had our own casualties too, of course. Despite what you read, battles are never one-sided. It seemed hours before I came upon a soldier of our own Thirtieth Regiment trying to take off an officer's jacket. It was Alec. The soldier, like me, assumed he was dead. I knelt to embrace him for the last time only to discover he was merely insensible. A small graze on his left ear was his only wound. I carried him back to camp and when he awoke he had no memory of the day's battle. When I told him the story of my discovering his body, thinking him dead, he paled and walked away. He's never referred to it since."

Tish shuddered. "And what is the change in him?"

"I believe he wants to put down his own roots at last."
George settled back in the chair, a comforting hand on her
shoulder.

"Lady Regina would be a fine match," Tish suggested in a
thin voice.

"The Incomparable and the Nonpareil," he agreed. "Why
not? They have much in common. And he cannot suspect
her of marrying him for his money for she has a fortune of
her own. That is not unimportant."

"George, I feel so alone," Tish admitted miserably. "So
alone."

He nodded. "I know what you mean. I've depended on
Alec. Since our days at Cambridge we've followed the same
course. But it's only natural for us to separate when we
marry." He halted at Tish's low groan.

"I don't mean between you and me, Tish." He looked in
consternation and confusion at her shuddering sobs. "Don't
cry, dear. Please, sweetheart." He sank down to the floor at
her side and patted her awkwardly on the shoulder. "I won't
have you unhappy, Tish. Is it the thought of my marrying
that makes you weep?"

Her head jerked up and she regarded him in horror. What
could she say?

"Is it, Tish?" he urged. He beamed when she nodded
slightly. "But there's no need," he declared with sudden deci-
sion. "You and I suit very well. We certainly like the same
things, fishing and walking in the hills. We both like the
Lake District and the life here. What better foundation for a
union?" He shook her gently. "Tish, look at me."

She raised a watery face.

"Marry me, Tish. I'll make you happy. I promise."

Pulling away, she tried to struggle to her feet but he
grabbed at her hand and held her back. "I—I must think,"
she gulped, choking back her tears.

"Of course," he smiled. "A lady is expected to behave shyly
at a proposal. But promise me I'll have your answer soon."

"I promise."

"Splendid. What a lucky thing I stayed home this evening. Now that I think of it," he chuckled happily, "I don't know why I didn't propose to you before, Tish. You're part of the Lakes. Can't have one without the other."

He chattered on excitedly of the future, suggesting a Grand Tour of the continent for a honeymoon, until Tish interrupted and begged him to keep his proposal a secret, at least until she had had time to consider it. Upon reflection, George agreed that it was only fair she should answer him before he spoke of it, but he warned her cheerfully that he expected her answer to be yes, and that he wouldn't wait long. With that pledge, Tish bade him a hurried good night and fled before he had a chance to kiss so much as her hand.

CHAPTER 13

Order was so much the rule at Lansdale Hall that coming across untidiness was as shocking as discovering a bear in the parlor. So when Lady Lansdale nearly stepped upon a tambour frame half covered with twists of thread, and right in the middle of the morning-room floor, she gasped in shock. Bending, she squinted nearsightedly at the mess. After a moment's reflection, she merely nudged the frame and tangle of silks with her toe of her slipper. Obviously Regina had gone into a rage over her embroidery. Or, more precisely, had gone into a rage while she was working at her embroidery. A wonder, Lady Lansdale mused, that the frame had not shattered to pieces for it had clearly been thrown down with force. Apparently the unsightly jumble pleased her, as she made no move to ring for the butler but glided on with a small smile.

From the doorway, unnoticed, she studied the group in the gold-and-rose drawing room. Reunited for the first time since the evening of the ball, they were remarkably constrained. Lord Lansdale and Tish were playing backgammon at a table by the glass doors. He was hunched over the board, seemingly lost in concentration, but she noted that he kept taking furtive peeks at his partner. That young lady's attention was riveted on the game, however, and she neither spoke nor looked up. Lady Regina, meanwhile, was rattling on to John Campbell, who made the appropriate noises of response but was noticeably distracted. From the mounting color in Regina's silken cheeks, she was well aware that Campbell's interests lay elsewhere.

Lady Lansdale, unconsciously pleating and unpleating the edge of her long black scarf, could not summon the energy to disturb the uneasy tableau. She frowned slightly as Regina gave a shrill, nervous giggle. That young lady was not in good looks today. Her passion for adding bits of false hair to her own golden glory had gone to extremes and she not only had a fantastic profusion of ringlets around her forehead, but a chignon of unbelievable proportions. She must be feeling insecure, Lady Lansdale surmised, for she normally had a sure sense of what became her and what did not. Ardenly had been conspicuously absent lately from the circle of admirers around the Incomparable Regina and that young lady was accustomed to having at least one lovesick swain at her elbow.

Tish, she judged, was for once at her best. She was tall enough to carry off her broad-brimmed straw bonnet, and the cerulean blue bow under her chin was tied at just the right cocky angle. Lady Lansdale recognized the blue pelisse from old but it had been updated with a set-in paisley patterned panel at the hem and she doubted that anyone else would know it for a third-season wrap. Yes, Tish looked charming. But pale.

Her eyes narrowing, Lady Lansdale studied her son. He was in high good humor but edgy. Not in one of the strange moods that had gripped him when he first came home, but on edge, expectant—but expectant of what?

Suddenly out of sorts and weary, Lady Lansdale forced herself across the threshold. Too many emotions upset her. She longed for her bed and solitude.

Upstairs, Ruddick was trying to capture Lord Ardenly's attention with scant success.

"I haven't the faintest idea as to the appropriate jacket for the occasion," Alec snapped at him for the second time. He was seated at a desk in the anteroom to his bedchamber, reading a letter which had just arrived from London by special messenger. "Just put out anything. I'll be done here in five minutes. The messenger is awaiting my reply." He scanned the sheets impatiently.

"Nothing in my experience prepares me for today, sir," Ruddick said severely. "These country antics are not our usual, my lord." His lordship paid him no heed so he stepped between the desk and the window, cutting off the light and effectively securing his lordship's attention.

"Move, man! Move aside. This chap's handwriting resembles a hen's scratchings. I can't make out one entire page."

"I was saying I have no guide for today's dress." Ruddick stood fast.

"And I don't give a damn what I wear," Alec shouted. "Just let me finish this letter. Now!" Slamming the pages onto the blotter, he ruffled through them until he came to the opening paragraph. "I see," he muttered. "That makes sense."

Wearing a martyred expression, Ruddick abandoned the room, conceding defeat, and opened the wardrobe in the bedchamber with a decisive jerk. Very well, if his lordship was so far gone in his wits that he would take no part in the selection, it was up to him. And fortunately, as both Ruddick and his lordship well knew, Ruddick had impeccable taste. He considered the row of exquisitely tailored jackets, from Weston's of course. The occasion was—what had Lord Lansdale's valet told him? A rushbearing ceremony? An annual custom, the fellow had said. The young women of the parish go to the tops of the hills to gather rushes and then carry them back to the church in Grasmere where they strew them on the floor. Ruddick thought the man had taken leave of his senses, but the fellow had explained quickly enough that the custom had, in fact, basis in need. The church floor was of soil. Moreover, burials were undertaken in the nave, which meant the ground was bound to sink and benches had to be constantly relocated. Ruddick paled at the mention of interments. He admitted, though, that the renewal of the sweet-smelling rushes was as much a necessity as a ritual.

What a gentleman wore to such a ceremony, Lansdale's valet had sneered, was obvious. He had not elaborated and Ruddick most certainly would not inquire. As he hesitated now in front of the wardrobe, he considered nipping down the back stairs and taking a look at Lord Lansdale, who was bound to be ready by now as it was past the prescribed meeting time. Pride forbade such sneaky action, however. Ruddick's hand shot out to the fawn-colored superfine. His lordship already wore brown, tight-fitting trousers tucked into his tasseled Hessian boots. Being late already, he would not want to change. Fawn was a perfect complement then. Sober, yet not funereal. And a white waistcoat with red trim.

When Ruddick reminded Alec that he was very late, his lordship swore under his breath at the interruption. "I need to send this note with the messenger," he instructed him. "The—the information I wanted is not complete. And do not fail to tell the messenger to ride hell-bent for leather. I want an answer immediately."

Ardenly's appearance when he finally went downstairs made Ruddick proud, but he still harbored a slight grudge that his lordship had not even glanced at himself once in the pier glass. For the fiftieth time, Ruddick heartily wished them both gone from the Lake District.

"Don't tell me you've been all this time achieving that splendid arrangement to your cravat?" George teased as Alec entered the drawing room. "Ardenly, you're worse than Beau Brummel. I vow you're a half hour late due to your wretchedly high sartorial standards. Is that the 'Orientale'?"

"'The waterfall,'" Alec shot back. "I beg your pardon, ma'am." He made his bow to Lady Lansdale. "Not my cravat but, rather, correspondence from London. An urgent business matter requiring an answer."

Lady Lansdale nodded with a smile but it was Regina who answered. "No matter," she purred, moving swiftly to his side and tucking her hand over his arm. "We are awaiting the queen. It seems we must all await Olivia's pleasure today."

"Olivia?" he repeated blankly.

"Didn't you know? Olivia is queen of the ceremony. Such a delightful conceit." She eyed Lady Lansdale with a frosty smile. "I understand you chose her, Lady Lansdale."

The older woman smiled back. "I did, my dear. Though there were other contenders, certainly. But Olivia's sweet enthusiasm for the region made her the logical choice. Don't you agree?"

"It is certainly your privilege to decide," Regina replied with considerable hauteur. "I must own I am surprised to find someone as sophisticated as yourself taking part in village frolics."

The Dowager returned her cool stare measure for measure. "This custom has been carried out in churches here since the Norse came across the seas in their longboats and converted to Christianity. It is in our blood, part of our heritage. George will be my stand-in today only because my poor health prevents me from actually attending the ceremony. But I ordered the greenhouse stripped to make nosegays for all the village girls and Olivia, as queen, shall bear a garland of our most precious blooms." She smiled malevolently. "I shall be the stick-in-the-mud, though I shall amuse myself while you all are away with my embroidery. Such a comfort to set a few stitches."

"You're not well, Mother?" George frowned.

She waved him away. "Nothing to concern yourself about. I can contrive well enough. As you may have heard," she turned to John Campbell, "after the rushes are carried to the church and the queen has placed the garland on the pulpit, you are met at the door by a fiddler who plays before the crowd as it parades to the public house. And after the dancing and celebration, I shall expect you all to join me here for dinner."

"You forget the gingerbread," George grinned.

"Alec and I are quite the outsiders," Regina smiled, taking Ardenly's arm once again. "Is there an eating custom also?"

"There is usually food associated with traditional rites," Lady Lansdale said dryly. "Grasmere gingerbread is famous as 'rushbearers' cake.'"

"And don't forget the gooseberry fool," Tish laughed, "that's George's favorite."

"Why, Tish and George know each other so well," Regina cooed, "they're like brother and sister."

"Not exactly brother and sister," George stammered, looking crossly at his houseguest. "But we go back a long way. Remember when you were queen of the rushbearing, Tish?"

"How charming," Regina persisted. "To think that we will have the former queen and the present one in our midst. Just how many years ago did you hold the honor, Tish?"

"So many that I've forgotten," Tish snapped.

"Your charming air of naïveté makes one forget that you are past your first season."

"Whatever she is, she's a dandy backgammon player." George took Tish's hand to help her rise and then kept a firm grasp on it as she hesitated and would have moved away. "Beat me two out of three games. Which is my usual run of luck with her."

"Quite a bluestocking, our Tish," Regina giggled.

Tish bit back a sarcastic retort when she saw Alec's long mouth curved in a derisive smile at the prospect of two females scratching one another. She mumbled something about the weather.

"Beautiful day, beautiful girl," George beamed.

"It's nice to hear compliments for a change," Tish said pointedly. She was enchanted to see Alec's amusement fade as George put an arm around her shoulders. She made herself smile coquettishly at him.

"Perhaps we should make a start," Alec said grimly.

"We await the queen," Regina reminded him, a trifle too gaily for the moment. "I declare that the folks hereabouts are rushed off their feet with festivities. I shall have to flee to London simply to rest," she laughed.

The jest elicited no answering laughter. Clearly flustered, Regina almost stamped her foot. "The queen is long coming," she said tartly, "though we must not complain."

John Campbell jumped to his feet, red-faced. "We do not know that Olivia is the cause of the delay."

"They have hardly been set upon by highwaymen," Regina sniffed, "and short of armed robbery, no excuse could suffice for an hour's tardiness."

"It might be wiser to await the facts before expressing an opinion," John Campbell shot back indignantly.

With a cold glance at George and Tish, Alec eased himself away from Regina and gave a curt bow to Lady Lansdale. "If you will excuse me, ma'am, it might be helpful for me to start ahead. Perhaps Olivia means to meet us en route. I could send you word if that is the case."

"That shows sense," she agreed. "You might as well all go on. Have a footman carry the garland for Olivia. You girls can gather your posies in the hall. The rest have been taken down to the village."

"I shall wait for Olivia here," John Campbell said stubbornly. "This is where we agreed to meet."

"And nothing must alter ancient customs," Regina muttered.

"Some of us find comfort in the age-old ways," Tish said angrily.

"All of you go!" Lady Lansdale sighed wearily. "If Olivia and her brother come here, I shall tell them where you've gone. Just go." She collapsed onto the sofa. What tempers! Tish and Alec glaring at one another. Campbell and Regina in a spat. Regina and Tish squawking. And the sugary Lady Regina was the burr under the saddle. She could guess why Regina was acting the shrew and she did not like it. It was too tiresome.

Even Olivia's placid countenance grew slightly troubled

when she arrived just then and felt the chill in the greetings. And after five minutes in the room, Olivia was wide-eyed. Regina's pointed sallies were not confined to Tish but hit home at both the Woffingtons. George, perplexed by Regina's ill-concealed bad humor, was not the only person relieved when the gentlemen finally had their top hats and walking canes, the ladies were suitably armed with parasols, shawls and nosegays, and the party could leave at last.

Trying to fill the heavy silence that surrounded the little procession as it made its way down to the village square, Hugh inquired about Saint Oswald. Olivia, he grinned, had given him a lecture about the rushbearing ceremony. It was always held, he remembered, on the Saturday closest to Saint Oswald's day, August fifth. But who was the worthy saint?

"A tenth-century monk," Tish said after George nudged her twice in the ribs. "And associated with the rushbearing probably because August fifth is high summer; the rushes on the fellsides are fully grown. Besides, it's a good time for a celebration as the two harvests, hay and wool, are both gathered in." She raised her voice. "The customs of our simple folk follow the cycles of nature. As even the most hen-witted person knows."

She lapsed back into silence as the party from Lansdale Hall joined the crowd in the village. She was soon smiling and laughing, however, as it was impossible for her to remain angry in the midst of such a cheery throng. The reserved, big-boned men and women of the District had little time for socializing, she mused, but when they did come together, they allowed their good spirits free rein. Without exception, they were almost boisterous in their merrymaking. Raising her face, Tish felt the combined warmth of the sun and coolness of a steady breeze. There was such glory in the simple pleasures of life, she couldn't remain morose. Gaiety is infectious.

Staying close to George, she felt safe enough in his presence to wave to a village girl driving a cow along in front of them from the well where she had been watering it. The girl prodded it from time to time with a long stick and stepped so lightly herself that she was almost dancing. Tish and George stopped to greet the Squire and to ask after his wife, who suffered from asthma.

Past the village square the men dropped off to the side and the girls took the center of the road, crossing the lush, flat green valley and heading for the western hills. Tish fell in with the rector's daughter and they laughed quietly over the latest romance novels. The excitement grew as the girls collected armfuls of rushes from the piles that had been prepared for them. Olivia was pushed to the front, Tish not far behind her, and she led the merry, chattering procession back down the hill and toward the whitewashed church.

The ceremony itself was simple and short. The rector said a prayer of thanksgiving for the plentiful harvest, the fertile land and the health of the people. Then, to the cheers of the crowd, he escorted Olivia to the church door.

The pleasure gardens of Vauxhall were a thousand years distant compared with the scene in the village square, which was more like a rustic medieval fair. There were cloggers and dancers, musicians with fiddles and tin whistles, wrestling and leaping competitions, booths of ale and "rushbearers' cake" and the promise of fireworks when the sun had set. Village maids did country dances with titled gentry, shepherds swung the schoolteacher and the rector's wife, and there was a general din of mirth-making and laughter. Even Regina succumbed to the charm of the day and smiled and danced with Alec with the same vivacious delight she had shown when she first arrived at Lansdale Hall. Tish felt a sinking heart to see Regina loose her claws. She herself whirled with friends and neighbors, even enticing Bowen to circle the floor twice. Hugh, Olivia and John traded partners, also, and romped as naturally as the rest. It was only Alec and Regina, Tish saw, who kept to themselves, dancing as happily as the others but exclusive partners for each other.

This colored Tish's pleasure in the afternoon and she made

no protest when George sought her out and suggested it was time to return home. The others were too exhausted to refuse either, and followed them up the hill. They overtook an old man halfway up who was leading his little granddaughter.

"Their steps suit," Tish whispered in George's ear.

He smiled and gave her a hug. "So do ours." He considered her flushed face. Her hat hung behind her back by the ribbons and her hair had come down and was streaming over her shoulders. She was less tidy than when the day started but infinitely more appealing to him. This was the Tish he knew. Comfortable. Easy. Taking a deep breath he blurted out, "Have you considered my proposal, Tish? Have you an answer?"

She shivered and looked around nervously. The five others were several paces back. Olivia and Hugh arm in arm, John Campbell at Olivia's side. And behind them, Alec and Regina. The setting sun was at their backs, shadowing their faces, but the silhouettes showed their heads close together. Just then Alec gave a shout of uninhibited laughter which sent a tremor down Tish's spine. Another shout of laughter and she turned to George, suddenly resolute.

After dinner they gathered on the wide marble veranda. Below them the fireworks display sent up puffs of color in staccato bursts.

"A minor display but prettily done," Lady Lansdale declared with satisfaction. She tapped her spoon against the fragile china of her coffee cup. "My son has an announcement," she said proudly.

It was official. Tish and George were to marry.

CHAPTER 14

There was a round of applause as Tish scrambled neatly into the gondola. "Speech! Speech!" Hugh exclaimed.

"Indeed, we must have a speech," George agreed.

Olivia led a fresh round of applause, beaming at Tish for a moment and then returning her eyes and attention to the smiling man at her side who held her hand tightly in his. She and John were obviously in love and Olivia had confided to Tish that he had asked her to marry him. He would accompany Olivia and Hugh home so that he might ask her father's permission for the marriage. There could be no possible objection: he had a comfortable income, a charming town house in London and a country estate of substantial size. Olivia was ecstatic.

Tish had squirmed uncomfortably under the weight of Olivia's high spirits. Three engagements at once, the girl had chirped. Herself and her John, Tish and George, and surely any day now they'd hear that Regina and Alec had come to an agreement. The romantic Lake District, Olivia said starryeyed; she'd never forget the Lake District.

It had required all of Tish's fortitude not to scream aloud. Pairing her name and George's was devastating, but linking Regina and Alec was worse. Her own romance, Tish admitted ruefully, would have to end and the sooner the better. She could not marry George. Through a succession of sleepless nights she regretted the recklessness which drove her to accept George's proposal when she knew very well she could never be his wife. What possessed her? Pique? Jealousy?

Loneliness? All three, she realized unhappily. Nevertheless, she liked him far too well to marry him.

Finding the words and opportunity to communicate that sad message had been impossible so far and already a week had passed since the rushbearing ceremony. For the first few days Tish's mother had been ill with a high fever and duties in the sickroom had consumed Tish's time. Then, just when her mother began to recover, her grandfather had announced that she might make her first free flight in the balloon. So Tish had turned her attention to that enterprise. The truth was that she welcomed the distraction, the excuse for a delay in confronting George. She could not bear to think of hurting him.

Now all was in readiness for the great adventure and though Tish was ready for the flight, she was not ready for the audience confronting her. George had learned of the flight from Bowen and had brought Olivia, Hugh and John with him to witness the departure. Regina was too busy to come, he had said. And Ardenly had been stopped by a messenger from London who arrived at Lansdale Hall just as they were all leaving.

"Speech!" Hugh cheered.

"No speeches," Tish smiled. "Just *au revoir*. And thank you for this lovely send-off." She waved and then motioned Bowen to release the anchor rope.

"Wait, Tish," George shouted. "I told you Alec asked particularly that you wait for him to arrive. He said he'd be right along. And please to wait. I told you."

"No." She threw him a quick smile to soften her blunt refusal. "We must take advantage of the calm, George. I'm sorry."

"Ardenly was damned emphatic, Tish. Please, my dear, just a moment or two longer. Surely that can't hurt?" he appealed to Tish's grandfather.

"She is in charge," the old man grumbled. "That is as it should be."

Nanny, glowering from the barn door, cleared her throat loudly but said nothing.

"I'm sorry," Tish repeated. "Bowen, untie the rope." She glanced up as the clatter of approaching hooves on the road announced another spectator. She shivered and her hands trembled on the valve rope as she adjusted it. Instinctively she knew she had to hurry.

"Quickly," she urged Bowen. "Cast off, quickly."

To her great exasperation Bowen only nodded and continued to move with characteristic deliberation, methodically, slowly.

"Come on, man," she said breathlessly. "Before he—"

Even as she spoke, Tarquin galloped into the yard, Ardenly jumped down, was over to the basket and inside in one swift motion. At that same instant Bowen let loose the line and the balloon shot up.

"How—how dare you?" Tish raged in a choked voice, glaring at her smiling passenger.

"I should have thought that by now you would realize I dare a great many things," the tall man grinned. He glanced down. "I don't mean to tell you your business, but hadn't you best attend to the balloon and vilify me at a more opportune time?"

Clenching her fists so tight the nails left pink crescents on her flesh, Tish closed her eyes, took a deep breath, and muttered, "Stand over there. Just stand over there and keep out of my way."

He moved without a word and she busied herself in rearranging the boxes of instruments and bags of ballast for better balance with the additional weight Ardenly provided. Barometer and compass were propped against the basket of food. Her watch hung by a ribbon around her neck. From a large flannel bag she took a black-bound notebook and pencil to note altitude, direction and time. That done, she looked around.

A laugh bubbled up from deep in her throat and exploded into the air. "We're up," she chortled. She spun in a full circle, hands waving exultantly. "We're absolutely, without doubt, truly and finally up! Or I should say the world is going down. Just look at it!"

Alec smiled just as broadly, his eyes busily taking in the vast panorama shrinking beneath them. "When he bestrides the lazy-pacing clouds, and sails upon the bosom of the air," he quoted. "And so are we, sailing upon the 'lazy-pacing clouds.'"

"The wonder of it," Tish murmured reverentially. She checked the barometer again. "Four thousand feet. I cannot credit it."

"How high will we go?"

She wrinkled her nose at the "we," jolted from her pleasure to the reality of Alec's presence, his intrusion into her private adventure. "*I* have planned to ascend to six thousand feet." She peered at him suspiciously. "What are you doing here, anyway?"

"Tish, Tish," he implored her, "let's not quarrel now. I know how long you've waited for this trip. Don't let me spoil it for you. That's certainly not my intention—and it would be a miserable waste of the opportunity."

The struggle of her emotions showed clearly in her expressive face and he could see how much she wanted to stay angry with him, how infuriated she was with his high-handed presumption, but he said nothing more. He knew his girl and she was too honest, too generous not to admit the truth of what he said. He wasn't disappointed.

Her concession was reluctant but total. "I shan't be a poor sport. You're here and there's little I can do about it." She smiled ruefully. "Other than pitch you over, and you're a shade too big for that." She bent over the instruments. "We're high enough. Six thousand, four hundred feet." She pulled the valve rope to open the vent, allowing gas to escape. "Yes . . . we've stopped ascending. There's a map in that box over there. I plan to chart our course as well as keeping other records."

Squinting at the compass she complained, "Sun's reflecting so I can't quite make it out." She cupped it in her hands. "Southwest." She hesitated as Alec handed her the map. "You can look at it first," she offered.

He smiled down at her and the warmth and approval in his eye sparked red flags on her cheeks. "I'll look second," he said softly. "You're in charge here, Tish, I take your orders."

She giggled nervously. "That's a change."

"You see what a taming effect you have on me," he smiled.

She felt herself grow even warmer and to hide her confusion, bent over the map.

"Southwest. . . ." She cocked her head at the compass again. "No, now we're going straight south. About here, I should judge." She reached for the telescope. "Yes, there's the coast of Morecambe Bay. See, there."

"How fast do we go? I get no sense of motion at all. If it weren't for my view of the changing landscape I'd think we were suspended totally still."

"Of course. We move with the wind so there's no sensation of motion. Actually, right now we're not going much faster than Tarquin could gallop." She looked up with an impish grin. "Now, that would be more appropriate. You down there, riding hell-bent for leather as a good Corinthian should, and me up here bumbling aimlessly through the sky."

"No indeed," he smiled dangerously. "I dare not lose you in the clouds so I forsake Tarquin and follow."

"Poor Tarquin," she laughed. Another exclamation of delight escaped her lips as she gestured to the north. The bracken which was foaming pale green in May had turned dark emerald in August and the vivid color splashed over the landscape, making it an emerald view to the north except for the splotches of gold where fields were given to hay grass.

The marshy shores of the Bay were a contrast in brown and gold.

"Now that is what I'd call modest grandeur," Alec said. Somehow he was at her side, his arm around her waist, his shoulder a pillow for her head. When his cheek brushed against the crown of her head, he sighed, "like soft silk."

"*Le petit oiseau*," Tish said quietly. "How nonchalantly the little bird flies on this miraculous escape. And how still the world is here. Still and calm. The horizon a blurred circle several hundred miles away." She looked up under her lashes. "I'm glad you're here," she said impulsively.

Catching her chin in his hand, he tilted her face up and dropped a soft kiss on her lips. Then, with surprising urgency, pulled her closer into his arms and bent his head again for a kiss so deep, so wild, that it shook Tish totally.

"I . . ." she pushed him away in instinctive self-defense. "I'm . . . starving."

At that he burst into laughter. "For what?" he managed to gasp. "If you mean to imply I'm not being satisfactory, I shall insist on trying harder. Though this is an original place to make love." He reached out for her.

Shaking her head violently, she edged away, grasping at the basket's rail for support to her quivering knees. "Too original," she blurted out. "And, as you said of my scolding, not an opportune time. No . . ." she warned, as he advanced toward her. "I mean it, Alec. I do not mean to be distracted again."

"Very well," he capitulated. "I will be patient. But I mean to have you." He studied her gravely though there was an urgent, bright light in his eyes. "Be advised, my sweet, green girl. I mean to have you in the end."

Tish gulped back a retort and pointed at the basket. "Nanny packed enough lunch for twelve."

"And being that you are the commander, it falls to me to spread the feast." He laughed boyishly, "A picnic at six thousand feet. You are never, my love, ever dull."

Using one of the cases as a table, he set out a bread-and-giblet pie, a roasted chicken, brown bread, apples, and the traditional bottle of champagne.

"Only one glass," he mused, adding with a mischievous chuckle, "may my lips drink where yours have touched?"

"Ardenly!" she said reprovingly.

"Sorry." He threw up his hands with disarming abandon. "I promise. Friends, nothing more. For the trip, anyway."

True to his word he kept the conversation light, exploring, with no suggestion of criticism, every facet of ballooning and plumbing the depths of her knowledge of the field. He was impressed, he told her candidly, with the thoroughness of her study.

"But why are you so curious?" she finally asked.

"Because you care about it," he answered simply.

That reply touched Tish as flowery compliments had not, and she was reduced to scanning the scenery until she recovered her composure.

"Well?" she prompted. "How do you feel about air travel now?"

"It's irresistible," he confessed.

Tish chortled with pleasure at his admission and then lifted her glass to salute the sky. "No bridges, no toll gates, no fences, no passports. Perhaps this will be the travel of the future. Balloon taxis, caravans of balloons crossing the vast oceans and deserts, small, personal vehicles," she added dreamily, "to take one shopping."

"Charming daydreams but rather impractical, as there is no way of directing the contraption. A vital drawback." The rebuke was softly spoken as if the stern-faced man could not bear to totally shatter her illusions. The glow of wonder in her face inspired him with a consuming desire to show her the greater wonder of love, while the intimacy of their solitude was a goad to his passion.

Stretching his long arms, he made a show of moving

around the gondola, repacking the dishes, consulting the barometer, and, hopefully, shaking off his pointless frustration. He was no green boy, he rebuked himself, to be so uncontrolled. He scowled to see that Tish was apparently indifferent to his presence. She was businesslike and efficient as she moved around the gondola, adding notes to the record book. It was maddening, he fumed. Finally he could bear it no longer. Pricked by her coolness, he succumbed to the temptation to take some small revenge. At least he would shake her out of that infernal composure.

"You will not take offense," he said, "if I point out that the balloon is a very feminine object. Not simply the matter of being without self-direction, you understand, although that is held to be a female trait. But you will observe that the great globe of gaily colored silks has an elegant curved line much like the female breast and, uh, nether region." He was delighted and encouraged by the shocked stare with which she regarded him. "Its wayward habits," he continued, "its ephemeral beauty, its unreliable charm, all are qualities more associated with the fair sex rather than my own."

"Perhaps," Tish flashed, "but it also carries one to a dreamland that is unlike anything in the world."

"Agreed. A woman, the right woman, can do that. But so can the right man in the reverse circumstance. Which is precisely what I intend to teach you."

Tish's startled eyes dropped away. This was out of her depth. "You forget your promise," she said in a small voice.

"No, madam," he said curtly. "You should know that I do not. Not for a single moment. I wish . . ." He half turned so that he was facing away from her and when he went on, it was in a normal, matter-of-fact tone. "I will not tease you more. Tell me about your real-life heroine. The other Letitia. You mentioned her when we first met."

She glanced up, surprised. "I didn't think you'd remember."

"I do," was all he said.

"She was very unafraid. That is the most impressive part of it all. She was portly, as I told you. An actress. And a spirited, adventurous lady who had considerable trouble convincing anyone that she should be a passenger in the balloon. She enjoyed every moment of her flight, was never the least bit fearful, and lectured afterwards and wrote a pamphlet about her experience. I have a copy of it at home, if you'd like to read it." Her voice trailed off.

Again taking measurements and readings, they were, she told him, going southwest and by all her calculations and readings of the map might be somewhere over York. A town to the west was miniature, the black roof of what was probably a church being no larger than a matchbox. By studying the course of the rivers and gleaning more detail through the telescope, they might pinpoint whether the town was Harrogate or Leeds. She agreed when he noted that the wind had dropped considerably. By her watch they had been aloft more than three hours. During the next hour they hung almost stationary over a ribbon about six yards long and two inches wide that they eventually identified as the River Aire. A little to one side of it, a little to the other, they might have been tied to the water for all it seemed to hold them in place.

"We might try descending a bit," Tish ventured after they had hung thus, in one place, with the silence between her and Alec growing ever more uncomfortable and heavy. "Wind currents are different at different altitudes, you know. And it's like swimming when the currents are different temperatures. You can move through warmth or coolness."

"A shade more westerly the winds," Alec said without expression, "and we'll eventually find ourselves over the North Sea." He refused to meet her eyes. "Not a welcoming landing spot, do you think?"

"Oh, we shall come down long before that," she informed him with studied breeziness. "With you along I won't plan to fly through the night. A disappointment, as I had hoped to travel over Manchester after dusk so that I might see the gas lights of the factories. I hear tell they are nine stories high and brightly illuminated at night."

Torn between a desire to box her ears and a desire to kiss her Alec said dryly, "Pray do not curb your spirits on my account. Although I am not the intrepid balloonist you are, my small experience on the battlefields has served to harden me just a little and I believe I have the pluck for the venture."

She bit her lip in vexation. He sounded furious with her. And the turn in the conversation reminded her of the argument they'd had by the lake when she had virtually accused him of cowardice. To her regret. In truth they had argued at virtually every meeting. Odious man. So charming, so amusing, so impeccable. She studied him under the cover of brown hair falling over her face. There wasn't a wrinkle or smudge on his light-gray trousers, not a one, nor a scrape to dull the shining boots. He might have just come from the ministrations of his valet. Even his black hair fell just right in purposeful disarray over his forehead. While she . . . Tish sighed deeply. She'd scraped her knuckles against the rough bags of sand, her hair was wild—

"How is your father? I cannot recall where he is serving at the moment?" Alec asked suddenly.

"He is, uh, changing posts. That is, I have not heard where he is to go. Do you think the wind is picking up? Shall we descend?"

He looked at her curiously with a strange, unreadable expression. "I wish you would confide in me," he said soberly. "I admire your independence. It is one of your qualities I most admire and find a refreshing change from the hang-about chits of our society. But it can be carried too far." He waited but Tish remained silent. "I will confide something in you then," he persisted. "I am of a different mind than when I first rode into the Lake District. What did you say you find in nature? Solace? I now see that. There indeed is a healing in the peace and harmony of nature. You were correct and I was wrong."

Whatever reply she might have made was cut short by a splatter of rain against the balloon which made sharp, pinging sounds. Lifting her face, Tish felt her cheeks sprayed. It wasn't the rain that alarmed her, however, but the ominous dark clouds. "A thunderstorm! We must descend. Electrical storms are very dangerous!"

"I distracted you," Alec frowned. "I did not mean to."

"Never mind." She moved to box the instruments. "I fancy that whenever we are together the sparks must fly, one way or another."

He flashed her a grateful smile but his expression did not lighten. To his mind, the situation was ominous. As far as one could see to the west, and gathering quickly to the north, were mountains of black clouds, monstrous billows of ebony bubbling up higher and higher like the brew of a witch's pot. An earthbound view of an electrical storm has a sort of wonder about it. The noise of the thunder, according to one folk tale, is Papa God moving furniture. Each culture has its own interpretation to soothe its children. But there is respect, all the same, for the unleashed power and random danger such a storm brings. And when viewed at its own level, confronted straight on, the sight is terrible and there is no blithe explanation for it.

"I've opened the valve," Tish whispered, her voice dropping instinctively. "We are descending."

Alec could not resist putting his arm protectively around her shoulder. "This is a fitting climax to the adventure," he said encouragingly. "We'll land safely."

"Of course," she shivered. They were both soaked to the skin and the early night was cool. "Will you distribute the bags of ballast? Five on one side and five on the other. Wedge the boxes behind them." Her voice shook slightly.

He moved to obey and then returned to her side. "It would

be no disgrace to be afraid," he said carefully. "The bravest soldiers are those who feel fear but carry on despite it."

The clouds advanced on them with incredible speed and seemed now to stretch from the highest heavens to the very earth itself. Although the basket and balloon were descending as rapidly as possible, still the clouds descended also and blackened the landscape.

Tish hesitated. "I should be afraid, I suppose—but I confess I think it's rather exhilarating."

Giving a shout of laughter, Ardenly hugged her tightly. "That's my girl. You are an Incomparable, my love. But, now, tell me what else I should do. You are in command here."

"Then I must take advantage of the moment," she chuckled, "for this is not likely to occur again." She took a deep breath. "When I tell you, let go the grapnel. With any luck it will snag a soft tree."

A crack of lightning almost overhead made them both jump.

"Better than fireworks," Alec murmured against her ear.

The aerial display had them spellbound, too hypnotized by the deafening thunder and erratic flashes of white through the dark whirlpool to be anxious.

"We must take opposite sides of the basket," Tish went on. "And when I give the word, let drop four of the bags of ballast. That is to ensure that we don't crash like a rock against the ground."

"Yes, ma'am," Alec smiled. He gave her another firm hug and dropped a soft kiss on her wet forehead. "That's for luck," he whispered, moving to take up his position.

Tish dragged a hand across her eyes to clear them of rain. The downpour was blinding and with that and the blackness of the storm, the occasional bursts of lightning were invaluable guides to a safe landing place. If they should chance to come down in a river, or a thicket of trees or— She scanned the ground anxiously.

"I think I see a clearing there," Alec shouted over the howling wind.

She peered into the inky air. "Where?"

"There, to the right."

For several long, awful moments Tish could not make out the spot but then it rose up before her, coming up too quickly. She looked across at Ardenly. His eyes were on her face and he was poised with the grapnel in hand, not looking at the ground but rather waiting for her signal.

Timing was crucial. If they dropped the ballast too early, there would be no way of giving their balloon additional lift except for the last two bags. And once those were dropped, there was no way to slow their descent. Unless they tossed over their clothes, as she had done on that day that now seemed a lifetime away—the day she had first met Lord Ardenly. She bit down on her lower lip, counting to herself, "One, two, three, four." Then aloud, "Now! Grapnel and ballast. Toss all the ballast. Now." And she bent for the bags at her own feet.

Some one hundred feet below the basket the iron grapnel caught on a bush and jerked the basket to a jolting stop, then tore loose and in a fit of jerks and stops caught and then tore loose across a wide meadow of scrubby bushes. The gondola at the end of the line bounced and thudded to the ground and bounced again like a dead weight on a fishing line in choppy waters. Buffeted from side to side as though a wild bull were charging the gondola, tossing it off his horns, then charging again, Tish and Alec were at the mercy of the elements.

Unable to keep her grasp on the basket's rim, Tish slid across the floor and bumped unceremoniously into Alec. He grabbed her before she could scramble away and buried her head against his chest, cushioning her body as well as he could with his own. The motion of the gondola was so violent that it was all Tish could do to cling to him, which saved her the worst of the impact though even so the barometer case dealt her a sickening shock in the side and the basket of food shooting across the floor slammed like a fist against her back.

Just as abruptly as it began, the wild ride ended. The grapnel must have finally caught a strong tree for it suddenly held firm and the basket, after one last teeth-rattling, bone-cracking thud, settled to the earth. The rain had, in the meantime, lightened to a drizzle as the storm moved off. Thunder and lightning continued but with growing spaces between outbursts and each time more distant.

Drenched, exhausted and bruised, Tish huddled against Alec, too shattered by the violence of the landing to move.

"Are you hurt?" he asked breathlessly.

"No," she choked, "I don't think so. Every bone in my body aches but nothing's broken." She wiggled her limbs experimentally.

"Thank God," he said with a ragged sigh. When he finally caught his breath, his voice was as calm as though they were sitting on the petit-point sofa in the gold-and-rose drawing room at Lansdale Hall.

"It is a joy to have you in my arms, my love, but I must trouble you to move. I fell back upon the largest of the boxes in that last bounce and I suspect several of my ribs are cracked."

And with that, he fainted.

CHAPTER 15

So fierce was the set of his shoulders, so grim was his expression, so angry the words he muttered under his breath as he came down the narrow staircase that Tish felt her heart stop and she actually saw black for one long minute. The doctor harrumphed loudly as he stomped past her into the kitchen and when he closed the capacious black bag holding his instruments, it was with a deliberate crack that was as ominous as his demeanor.

Clutching the doorframe for support, Tish croaked, "Is he dead?"

The doctor glared at her. His black cape boasted half a dozen layers and he loomed as threatening in the flickering light from the fire as a rabid bat. "Eh?" he snorted. "Speak up. What's say?"

"Is he dead?" Tish croaked, but more loudly.

"What's red?" the beady eyes darted around the room. "Red, you say?"

"Dead!" Tish shouted in anguish. "Is he dead?"

"You mean him?" he gestured toward the ceiling. "Not unless being a blockheaded, stubborn idiot kills. And in my long professional experience I've yet to come across a case of death by pigheadedness." He cackled gleefully. "That's a good one."

"But you look so—" she raised her voice again almost to a shout. "You looked so angry as you came down."

He searched through his pockets until he extracted a grimy candy which he popped into his mouth. "Who wouldn't be angry?" He cocked his head inquisitively at the farmer's wife coming in from the yard, her arms laden with firewood. "Who wouldn't be angry?" he asked her. "Called from my bed in the middle of the night to attend to a raving madman who descends from the sky and then hasn't the good sense to listen to my prescription."

"But what ails him?" Tish insisted.

"Cracked ribs, bang on the head, nothing serious. Head's hard as iron. I prescribed bed rest, a diet of gruel and barley water, and application of leeches to remove excessive bleeding. To which your fine gentleman answers 'nonsense.' Nonsense, indeed. Said he would be up in the morning, wanted ale and a hearty breakfast, and thought leeches were a relic of the barbarians! You the daft female that landed with him?" She nodded and he plowed on, fastening his cape, picking up his bag and making for the door. "Then you're probably as crazy as he is and I won't waste my breath. He wants to see you. Don't fuss over him, woman, he'll mend all right. Have a devil's own headache for a day or so," he chuckled. "And I should lay off the hugging for a bit. Not with a fellow what has cracked ribs, anyway."

Tish would have blushed at that last remark but she was not present to hear it. When she learned that nothing serious was wrong with Alec, she had picked up her skirts and scurried for the stairs. Once outside his door, however, she was attacked by a case of shyness and she paused on the threshold, her hand arrested in mid-air.

"Tish? Is that you? Come in," he called.

"I'm on my way to bed," she replied in a wavery voice. "Good night."

"Don't you dare go away, my girl. Come in. Now."

"It's late. I'm tired . . . I'll see you in the morning."

"If you don't come in, I'll come out," he threatened.

She looked about anxiously but the farmhouse was in silence. The sleepy farm woman whom she had hauled out of bed had returned to her rest. Her husband had retired the instant he carried Alec back to the house and set him down.

"Tish!" Alec said sternly.

"No. It's late and everyone's in bed. I'll see you in the morning."

She tiptoed down the corridor toward the room that had been given to her and stopped halfway, listening. She expected more of an argument than that but she was prepared to resist. Common sense told her that no good could come of a midnight visit to Alec's bedroom. A ghastly groan and strange gurgle came from behind her. Whirling, she ran back, wrenched open his door and flung herself down at his bedside.

Alec's eyes were closed, his arms outflung as though in fruitless supplication. Another low groan was the only sound he uttered.

"Alec, Alec, wake up. Wake up, my love." She chafed his cold fingers between her own, then clasped them to her cheeks to warm them. "Speak to me, my love. My dearest."

The limp arms suddenly sprang to life and imprisoned her in an embrace that drew her down across his chest until her lips were captured by his. "My love," he said thickly. "My own dearest green girl."

"Scoundrel." She pulled herself upright, ruthlessly pushing him back against the pillows at the expense of his aching ribs. Reluctantly he let her go.

"All's fair," he murmured. "And I am delighted to find you delighting in my restored health. Didn't that fool of a doctor tell you I was all right?"

She tried to stand up but he caught her wrist in a firm grip. "Now that won't fudge. I'll admit that once again we are not at an opportune time for making love. But I will not have you retreat entirely. We've come too far and there are matters which must be settled." He winced as she tried to pull free, which totally disarmed her and she sat back docilely.

"No more talking tonight, Alec. We are both exhausted. And if your aches are twice mine, and they must be that at least, what we both need is rest. We'll talk tomorrow."

He shook his head. "Tomorrow you'll be surrounded once again by your hovering guardian angels. I know your wily ways, my love, and once you have the chaperones back in place, your faithful Nanny, your good grandfather, your peerless Bowen, your . . . fiancé, I won't stand a chance."

"Whatever you say," she agreed quickly. Despite his cheerful tone his face was pale and strained, testimony to his sorry state. "But how should my so-called chaperones come here?"

"Did you think me lost to all reason because of a blow to the head?" he smiled wearily. "I gave the good farmer who took us in a princely sum to dispatch his steward with a message as to our whereabouts. And the steward's daughter, a comely lass named Alice, is even now snoozing on a pallet in your bedroom. I could not have you suffer because I was an uninvited passenger on your trip and willy-nilly we sleep under the same roof. It would be poor care I took of you if I did not make provisions for your reputation."

To her horror, Tish burst into tears at that and found herself lying again against his shoulder. Strangely enough his tender, soothing phrases and the gentle caress of his hand against her hair were at once comforting and disquieting and she cried all the harder for the conflict. At last the sobs quieted and she lay exhausted in his arms, drained by the fury of her weeping.

"I'd best rinse my face," she said in a muffled voice. Sitting up reluctantly she glanced shyly at him, then crept off the bed. The cold water from a pitcher in the corner was welcome. Distracted, she looked around. A small worn carpet, narrow bed and stool completed the furnishings of the tiny room. A humble farmhouse but welcome as a palace to Tish when she had stumbled away from the balloon in search of help.

"Now come sit so we can talk, Tish," Alec prodded her gently. The flickering embers cast a shadow across his face.

Nodding, she drew the stool to the bedside and sank down upon it. At his gesture, she put her hand in his and felt the reassuring grip of his fingers.

"Why did you cry?" he asked.

"I suppose because of what you said about taking care of me," she admitted. "It's not that my—my guardian angels don't care for me. They do, in a way. But for a long time, so long," she sighed, "I've felt that it was up to me to solve our troubles. After all, Nanny is old and hardly in a position to do anything. Nor is Grand-père. And poor Mama is . . . an invalid. Besides," she brightened a bit, "you have your own guardian angel in Ruddick, from what George tells me."

"True," he smiled, "but will you confide in me now, Tish?" The brown-green eyes bored into hers. Ardenly seemed nervous, she thought curiously. She had never seen him anything but in command, very much sure of himself.

"Confide?"

"Yes, now," he said urgently.

She looked away to the fire but then drew her eyes back resolutely and squared her shoulders. "I'll tell you," she laughed weakly, "for to tell the truth it will be a relief to have it out." Her expression softened at the look of pleasure he gave her.

"It has to do with the entail," she went on. "An entailed estate, as you know, passes from oldest son to oldest son. The exalted heir is, in effect, no more than a life tenant of the estate and cannot sell or mortgage the property except by an Act of Parliament. Ridiculous in the extreme, since it is very expensive to have an Act passed and therefore patently impossible for the heir who wishes to sell or mortgage, since he must be impoverished or he wouldn't need the Act in the first place. Round it goes like a circle and like a circle there is no way out. It costs money to get the Act, you can't sell without the Act, and the only one who wants to sell is already poor. Like a bad dream. It is, or can be, a trap.

"There is, of course, usually an annual income for the heir's wife and lump sums for daughters and younger sons when they come of age. And so it was with my father's estate. All entailed, income for Mama and a lump sum for me. Except that Papa gambled away all my mother's fortune and even the small bit left to me." Her lower lip trembled but she took a steadying breath and went on. "He did not advertise his weakness and few knew of it. He was most discreet. And most unlucky. Further and further into debt until nothing was left but this bit of farm here that had belonged to his father's family. We retreated here."

She raised her large eyes to Ardenly. "My father was waiting for another foreign post, hoping desperately to recoup the family fortune at least in part in that way. But before any notice came he caught a chill and became ill. I do not think he struggled much for his life. He lingered only a few days. After his death, my mother, who had never been very strong, took to her bed and has never left it. She suffers from insomnia and nightmares and resorts too often to laudanum to quiet her uneasy mind. Not the ideal parents, eh?" she finished bitterly.

"I thought as much," he answered calmly. "My trip to London was not for pleasure, my love. I knew that some secret worried you. The information brought to me today by messenger confirmed my suspicion. You see, I was vain enough to believe that you might have considered my proposal of marriage were it not for some trouble." He smiled tenderly. "You did not comprehend my tenacity, my girl."

"No." She blushed. "But that is not the worst of it. My parents' story is sad but I cannot find the heart to condemn them. My mother, even as a girl, mourned the life she left in France. She never felt at home in England and I suspect she married my father more for the refuge he offered than for affection. She was always, and I knew this even as a child, a stranger in the house. I couldn't understand quite what was wrong but now I see it plainly. And my father was a brilliant, energetic man who had money and so should have been content riding on his estate, going to his clubs in London and such. But he was restless. His parents strongly disapproved of his intention to enter the diplomatic service and he only did so when they had both died, and by then he was too old to make a success of it. Worse, the habit of gambling was too entrenched by then to pluck out. If they had both been born at different times, or different places, my parents might have met a better fate. My mother might have lived to a ripe old age in France, productive and well. And had my father been born of less noble blood, he might have been more enterprising and successful."

Alec gave her hand a reassuring squeeze. "I learned of your father's death on my last trip to London. And just before the flight a messenger brought me details of the estate settlement. Such records are available to the public but it is deuced hard to uncover them, which is why it took me so long to unravel your secret. Because the estate is entailed, you sought to keep your father's death a secret. So that the heir, some cousin or other, would not claim your Lake District haven."

"Exactly. It's so isolated here, we thought it might be years before the news came to anyone's attention. We live quietly. And father had only been here a few weeks when he caught cold. It's not that we wanted to cheat my cousin, you see. He is quite wealthy in his own right and this wee property would be nothing to him. But I met him in London and he is a most righteous, tight-fisted sort. I'm convinced he would have declared it his solemn responsibility to take charge of the farm here. And I'm just as positive he would have done his duty by us and would have found us a suitable cottage to live in. In the south, perhaps, or west. But not here. And I couldn't bear to leave," she cried in anguish. "I couldn't uproot Grand-père and the rest. Old people need familiar surroundings."

"Your father's story is not lost on me," Alec said quietly while Tish struggled to regain her composure. She raised a teary face. "Even I would not ascribe the adjectives to myself that you used for him. 'Brilliant,' for example. But it is true that a man of energy and wits needs a better outlet for his time than frittering it away aimlessly. I came to the Lake District to help George, who was troubled by his war memories, and also to help myself. And I think I have found my direction here." His hand lingered on her shoulder, running the long strands of hair through his fingers. "There are reforms needed on my estates that could occupy a lifetime," he smiled. "But I am reminded that you have not finished your speech."

"I don't know what you mean." She wiped away the last of the tears with a corner of the bedsheet to his vast amusement. "Well, I lost my handkerchief," she said indignantly.

"That's better," he grinned. "I don't recognize you when you're meek and mild. Now finish the confession. About the ballooning. I want no cobwebs between us."

Smiling at him tenderly, Tish chuckled. "Well, I intend to be the first woman to sail across the English Channel in a balloon. I shall procure the sponsorship of the London *Times* or some such publication to pay the costs. And then I shall write books and lecture on the subject."

"Like Letitia Sage," Ardenly groaned.

"Like Letitia Sage," she said defiantly. "When I am rich and famous we will not need my cousin's penny-pinching sponsorship. I can even buy the farm from him myself." She twisted the bedsheet between nervous fingers. "Sometimes I even let myself hope that my mama will get well again, someday when there is money enough for the expensive soaps and perfumes she longs for, when she has a dozen new silk frocks, like the old days. I worry that she is oppressed by the shabbiness of our house. It frightens her, reminding her of the days when she and her parents fled the revolution and were fugitives."

Alec's eyes narrowed as she went on and his grip on her wrist was tight as iron.

"You will understand now why I couldn't accept your proposal. I couldn't burden you with these worries, nor add such a drain to your purse."

He gave a shout of laughter which caused him to clutch at

his chest. "Sweet dunce," he smiled between clenched teeth, "is it conceivable that you know nothing of my circumstances?"

"What do you mean?" she said, bewildered.

"You admitted that you love me. When you thought me unconscious?" He smiled again when she said that indeed she did, but nothing in the world could persuade her to marry him. Assuming, she added in confusion, that he should deign to ask her a second time.

"But, my child, I am a very rich man." He raised himself with gingerly care up upon one elbow. "Truly, I am very rich. The result," he grinned, "of being the only male child and the heir to several bachelor uncles and aunts. I have enough fortune to sustain several dozen of your poor relations in the greatest luxury and not notice the cost." He shook her hand impatiently. "Look at me, Tish! Don't hide in that glorious hair."

She peeped from behind the cascade of brown locks. "You are very rich?" she faltered.

"Disgustingly rich," he beamed. "So that need not concern you. And I must own I find it welcome novelty to be regarded for my inner self alone."

"It is not entirely your inner self that pleases me," Tish said with a mischievous twinkle. "You are uncommonly handsome, my lord Ardenly."

"No . . . no," he roared with laughter, "pray do not make me laugh. It causes hell's own fury in my poor chest." He sank back slowly upon the pillows. "Now," he said firmly, "if the question of finances is settled, and you are assured that an alliance between us will not lead to my bankruptcy, what other impediments will you raise? For I know you, my girl, and you are not easily vanquished. Only please," he raised a hand, "a sip of water for the invalid and no more boisterous humors until I mend."

"Here. Well, there is the matter of my ballooning," she suggested tentatively, handing him a cup of water. "You cannot want a countess who has appeared on the lecture circuit and made a public spectacle of herself."

"Indeed I do not," he said promptly. "Which is why you will not do it." He eyed her speculatively. "But what about your fiancé? I cannot think it flattering to George that we debate your nuptials with me when you are fixed to marry another."

"I forgot for a moment," she said uneasily, shifting nervously on the stool.

"Never mind," Alec said cheerfully. "I said I would take good care of you and I meant it. I told George the night of the rushbearing ceremony that he should pay no heed to your acceptance. I explained that I meant to have you no matter what you might say. At first George was adamant but after a few days he listened to reason. We both agreed you require a husband with a—"

"How dare you!" She jumped to her feet, kicking the stool over with a loud clatter. "How dare you interfere in my life? I know what you were going to say. A firm hand on the reins is what I need. When will you understand that I am not a mare!"

He quirked an eyebrow. "We agreed you need a husband who is a romantic," he said calmly. "As I discover myself quite unexpectedly to be. George finally agreed that we would let you come to the truth yourself. He is excessively fond of you, you know."

After a peremptory knock, the farmer's wife poked her head in. "I heard a clatter," she frowned, "and voices raised." She stared at Tish, then at Ardenly. "Seems to me it's that time when each of us ought to be in his own room," she said darkly. "If you catch my meaning."

"Indeed, we do, Mrs. Brady," Ardenly said soothingly. "Lady Letitia was just fetching me water. An errand of mercy. Before you retire, madam," he inclined his head politely toward Tish, "I beg a reply to my query."

"We can speak about it tomorrow," Tish said stiffly. "Besides, you haven't asked me anything."

"You take my meaning nonetheless," Alec said with a slight smile. "Now is the moment. Will you or won't you?"

Tish looked about wildly. The farmer's wife, planted in the center of the room, hands on her hips, her dressing gown firmly knotted, obviously had no intention of leaving them alone again.

"Tomorrow," she beseeched him.

"I think not. Now. Please."

"What about Regina, the Incomparable?" Tish parried.

"A ploy to make you jealous. Not too subtle, either, but I was, for a long time, desperate."

There was a wealth of love in that admission and it gave Tish courage.

"The reply to your unspoken query is—yes."

"I am honored," Ardenly said softly. "If you will leave us for one minute, Mrs. Brady, I promise that the Lady Letitia will be along immediately."

Quelled by the quiet authority in his voice, the woman shuffled her feet and then turned with a flounce. "One minute," she said over her shoulder.

"No time to waste," Alec whispered with a wink. "Come here, my dearest green girl." He held her at arm's length for a moment. "My summer-sweet girl, my lake witch. You must tell them to pack *The Little Bird* with care."

"But why?"

"So that we can both enjoy the balloon later on private flights, my love. I would not keep you from your adventures entirely, but we shall share them."

The hug she gave him almost broke two more ribs and the kiss he gave her in return, while brief, held great promise.